Virgil O. Stamps'

FAVORITE
RADIO SONGS

A Collection of Sacred Songs, New
and Old, Compiled Especially
for Radio Programs by

VIRGIL O. STAMPS

•

•

Price: One Dollar

•

Order from

Stamps-Baxter Music Co.

Dallas, Texas — Pangburn, Ark. — Chattanooga, Tenn.

V. O. Stamps

Virgil O. Stamps

presents . . .

The Stamps Quartet

of

Dallas, Texas

Left to right: Rippetoe, Bacon, Gaither, Foshee
Seated: Joe Roper, Pianist

The Stamps Quartet is heard regularly on numerous radio stations—write for schedule, address: Virgil O. Stamps, P. O. Box, 4007, Dallas, Texas.

Look For Me, For I'll Be There

V. O. S.

Virgil O. Stamps, owner

Virgil O. Stamps

1. When you reach your home in glory,   Free from ev-'ry toil and care,
2. Christ, the Lord, has long been with me,   Shielding me from ev-'ry snare;
3. Won't it be a hap-py meet-ing,   When you meet your loved ones there
4. Won't there be a joy-ous sing-ing,   In that home so bright and fair,
1. When you reach your home, home in glo-ry,

Where the saved shall dwell for-ev-er,   You may look for me, for I'll
He will lead me safe to heav-en,   You may look for me, for I'll
In the home of end-less glo-ry?   You may look for me, for I'll
When the heav'nly choir as-sem-bles?   You may look for me, for I'll
Where the saved shall dwell, dwell, for-ev-er,

CHORUS

be there.... Look for me, (Oh, look for me,) Look for me, (For I'll be there;)

You will find me with the an-gels fair, Look for me,
You will find me with the angels fair,   Oh, look for me,

Look for me,   Don't for-get to look for me up there.
For I'll be there; Don't for-get to look for me up there.

No 2

Cling to the Cross

V. O. Stamps, owner.

Rev. Johnson Oatman, Jr.   Virgil O. Stamps

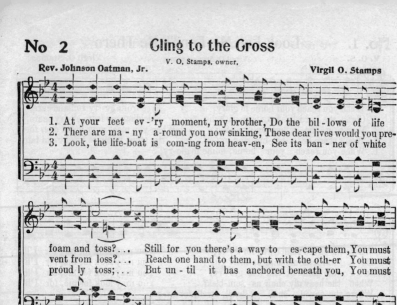

1. At your feet ev-'ry moment, my brother, Do the bil-lows of life
2. There are ma - ny a-round you now sinking, Those dear lives would you pre-
3. Look, the life-boat is com-ing from heav-en, See its ban - ner of white

foam and toss?... Still for you there's a way to es-cape them, You must
vent from loss?... Reach one hand to them, but with the oth-er You must
proud-ly toss;... But un - til it has anchored beneath you, You must

CHORUS

cling, cling, cling to the cross. You must cling, cling, cling to the old rugged cross,

cross,......

You must cling, cling, cling to the cross;........ No trouble can down you, no
cross, the rugged cross;

bil - low can drown you, If you cling, cling, cling to the cross...........
old rug-ged cross.

No. 3   Sunset is Coming but the Sunrise We'll See

J. R. BAXTER, JR.   in "Harbor Bells No. 6"   EUGENE WRIGHT

1. Pil-grims for Je-sus in a low-land of sin, Hop-ing that we at
2. Strangers, but hap-py in His vineyard to-day, Try-ing to help our
3. Wea-ry and foot-sore ere the bat-tle is won, Trust-ing the prom-ise

last the life-crown may win; Serv-ing the Master thru the morn-ing are we,
Lord and Sav-ior al-way; Serv-ing the Master thru the noon-time are we,
that we'll hear His "well done;" Serving the Master all the even-ing are we,

CHORUS

Sun-set is com-ing but the sun-rise we'll see.   Sun-set is com-ing but the

Heaven-ly beau-ty make the shad-ows to flee;   Glo-ry is

sun-rise we'll see,

Sun-set is com-ing but the sun-rise we'll see.

wait-ing when the spir-it is free,

No. 4 You Shall Reap What You Sow

N. W. Allphin   Virgil O. Stamps, owner.   Virgil O. Stamps

Male Quartet

1. Broth-er, what of the seed you are sow-ing, As a-long your way you
2. Do you sow to the flesh or the spir-it, As you tread this vale be-
3. Thot's and words for a harvest you re sow-ing, In-to deeds they'll sure-ly
4. Is your sow-ing for glo-ry and hon-or? Will it be for weal or

go? (your way you go?) You should choose them with care-ful-ness, knowing, You shall
low? (this vale below?) Do you hope end-less joy to in-her-it? You shall
grow; (they'll surely grow:) Ei-ther blessings or curs-es be-stow-ing, You shall
woe? (for weal or woe?) By and by when your har-vest you gar-ner, You shall

rit.   REFRAIN

reap...... just what you sow. You shall reap.... what you
You shall reap just what you sow.......... You shall reap

sow,..... You shall reap ... just what you sow; ... Oh, "be not de-
what you sow, You shall reap what you sow;

ceived, for God is not mocked," You shall reap just what you sow.........
You shall reap just what you sow.

No Tears In Heaven

R. S. A.

Robert S. Arnold

1. No tears in heav-en, no sor-rows giv-en, All will be glo-ry in that land; ..... There'll be no sad-ness, all will be gladness, When we shall join that hap-py band.....

2. Glo-ry is wait-ing, wait-ing up yon-der, Where we shall spend an endless day; ..... There with our Sav-ior, we'll be for-ev-er, Where no more sor-row can dis-may.....

3. Some morning yon-der, we'll cease to pon-der O'er things this life has brought to view; ..... All will be clear-er, loved ones be dear-er, In heav'n where all will be made new.....

CHORUS

No tears, ... no tears, no tears up there, Sor-row and pain will all have flown; .... No tears, ... in heav-en fair, no tears, no tears up there, No tears in heav-en will be known. ...

Endless Joy is Coming

James Rowe

Claude Goodman

Slow

Hum

1. Tho' a bur-den bearing, nev-er be de-spair-ing, Ev-er on the bless-ed
2. Now we bend in sorrow, but when dawns the morrow, Nevermore our souls will
3. Storms to-day may sweep us, but the Lord will keep us, We shall have His presence

Hum

Faster

Hum

Lord re-ly; Trusting Him completely, do His bidding sweetly, End less joy is
grieve or sigh; In the land of glo-ry we shall sing the sto-ry, End-less joy is
ev - er nigh; He will be be-side us to up-hold and guide us, End-less joy is

Hum

End - less

REFRAIN

com-ing, com-ing by and by. Endless joy is coming, com-ing by and by,
coming by and by,

joy is

When we reach the city that is built on high, forever To the promise clinging, as we

travel homeward singing, Endless joy is coming, coming by and by.
For an end - less joy is

No. 8 I've Been List'ning in on Heaven

THOMAS RAMSEY · in "Harbor Bells No. 5" · VIRGIL O. STAMPS

1. I have had a hap-py vis-ion Of a dis-tant bet-ter land,
2. When my courage has been shak-en, And the blue skies turn to grey,
3. Tune your heart to heaven's wave-length, Thru the blest con-trol of pray'r,

There was not a sign of sor-row, Glad-ness ruled on ev-'ry hand;
E-vil forc-es oft-en tempt me, Try to turn me from the way;
Ground your faith in love e-ter-nal, Tune out sor-row pain and care;

Mu-sic flowed in sweet-est con-cords, 'Twas an end-less day of spring,
But there's something that will com-fort, Peace and glad-ness it will bring,
In the time of in-ter-fer-ence, Clos-er to the Sav-ior cling,

I've been list-'ning in on heav-en, Just to hear the mil-lions sing.
When I'm list-'ning in on heav-en, Just to hear the mil-lions sing.
While you're list-'ning in on heav-en, You will hear the mil-lions sing.

CHORUS

I've been list-'ning in on heav-en, List-'ning to the songs of love,
List-'ning,............ List-'ning,............

I've Been List'ning in on Heaven

Sung by saints of all the a - ges, Prais-ing Christ in heav'n a - bove;

I've been list-'ning in on heav - en, And I heard their mu - sic ring,

List-'ning,.............. List-'ning,..........

I've been list-'ning in on heav - en, Just to hear the mil - lions sing.

No. 9   Windham

DANIEL READ

1. Broad is the road that leads to death, And thousands walk to - geth-er there,
2. "De - ny thy-self, and take thy cross," Is the Re - deem-er's great command;
3. Lord, let not all my hopes be vain; Cre - ate my heart en - tire - ly new,

But wis-dom shows a nar-row path, With here and there a trav - el - er.
Na - ture must count her gold but dross, If she would gain this heavenly land.
Which hyp-o-crites could ne'er at-tain, Which false a-pos-tates nev-er knew.

Paradise Valley

in "Thankful Hearts"

VIRGIL O. STAMPS

1. As I trav - el thru life, with its trou-ble and strife, I've a glo - ri - ous
2. As I roam the hill-side, or I list to the tide, As I pluck the sweet
3. Tho your garden is rare, it is naught to com-pare With the flowers that

hope to give cheer on the way; Soon my toil will be o'er and I'll rest on that shore
flowers that grow in the dale; A faint picture is there of a land bright and fair
bloom in the garden a-bove, In the midst of it grows Sharon's perfect sweet Rose,

Where the night has been turned in-to day.
Where per - en - ni - al flow-ers ne'er fail.
'Tis the won-der-ful Flow-er we love.

CHORUS

Up in the beau-ti - ful
Up in par - - a - dise

par - a - dise val - ley, By the side of the riv - er of life,........
val - ley ...... of the riv - er of life,

Up in the val-ley, the won-der-ful val-ley, We'll be free from all
Up in par - - a - dise val-ley, ...

Paradise Valley

pain and all strife;.....   There we shall live in the rose-tinted garden,
from   all pain and all strife; There we'll live in the gar-den,......

'Neath the shade of the ev-er-green tree,...... How I long for the par-a-dise
of   the ev-er-green tree,   for   the

val-ley, ...   Where the beau - ty of heav-en I'll see.........
par-a - dise val-ley,   beau - - - ty   of heav-en I'll see.

No. 11   Crossing the River

H. M. Eagle, owner   H. M. Eagle

1. Cross-ing the riv - er, Bound for the heav-en-ly shore, Pain gone for-ev-er,
2. An - gels are sing - ing Wel-come upon that bright strand, Joy-bells are ring-ing
3. Some morning, yonder, When all our tri-als are o'er, Where hearts are fonder,

D. S.—*Tri - als all end-ed,*

FINE   REFRAIN   D.S.

Troubles and sorrows all o'er.
O - ver that beau-ti-ful land. Cross-ing the riv-er, Safe on the Sav-ior's breast,
We'll be u-nit-ed once more.

There all is per-fect   rest.

He Bore It All

J. R. Baxter, Jr.

Virgil O. Stamps

1. My pre-cious Sav - ior suf-fered pain and ag - o - ny, He bore it
2. They placed a crown of thorns up - on my Sav-ior's head,
3. Up Cal v'ry's hill in shame the bless - ed Sav - ior trod,

all .... that I might live; .... He broke the bonds of
By cru - el man with
free - ly bore it all   I with Him might live; Between two thieves they

sin and set the cap - tive free,   all that I might
spear His side was pierced and bled,
cru - ci - fied the Son of God, He bore it all that I might

FINE   **REFRAIN**

in His presence live. He bore it all   that   I might see His
live......... ....   Je - sus bore it all,

shin - ing face,   Free - ly bore it all
see His shin-ing face, He bore it all .... that I might

He Bore It All

I with Him might live; I stood condemned to die but Je-sus took my place,
live;.................. stood condemned to die free-ly took my place

No. 13   Sail On.

Lizzie DeArmond, Swarthmore, Pa.

J. R. BAXTER, JR., OWNER,

J. R. Baxter, Jr., Ft. Payne, Ala.

1. Sail on, O soul, tho' the waves dash high, And gath'ring clouds fill the evening sky;
2. Sail on, O soul, at your Lord's command, Just put the helm in your Father's hand;
3. Sail on, O soul, to the promised rest, Your Pilot's near and He knoweth best;

Tho' torn your sails with the tempest blast, You'll anchor safe to the Rock at last.
Trust all to Him whom the winds o-bey, His "Peace be still" shall your fears allay.
There's light beyond, soon the storm will cease, Press on, press on to the port of Peace!

REFRAIN.

Sail on, ... tho' the bil-lows roll, Sail on, ... He will keep your soul,
Sail on, sail on, Sail on, sail on,

You'll anchor safe when the storms are o'er, Sail on, O soul, to the Canaan shore.

No. 15 You Must Come in at the Door

sung on Victor Record, No. 21722, by Stamps and Yandell

Copyright, 1929, by V. O. Stamps and M. L. Yandell

Arr. by Stamps and Yandell

CHORUS

My Lord it's so high, you can't get o - ver it, So low, you can't get under it,

So wide, you can't go a - round it, You must come in at the door.

BASS SOLO

1. Good morn - ing, fel - low pil - grims,........ You ask me
2. You may talk about me, my broth - er,.......... Just as much as
3. You ask me what's the mat - ter with the church, That we can't
4. O the Bap - tists go by wa - ter,........ The Meth-o - dists

where I'm bound, I'm trav' - ling to a
ev - er you please, But if I men - tion your
hear a shout, There are sin - ners in the a - men
go by land, But I tell you, friends, if you

D. C.

beau - ti - ful land, There to wear a robe and crown.
name at all, It'll be when I'm on my knees.
cor - ner, my friend, That ought to be turned out.
want to get to heav'n, You got - a go hand in hand.

The City of Gold

and the city was pure gold, like unto clear glass.—Rev. 21: 18

Adger M. Pace

W. Z. Kitts

1. In the Bi - ble we read of a cit - y Where the faith - ful shall nev - er grow old; I have heard that its won - der - ful road-ways Are built of the pur - est of gold.

2. On the Is - land of Pat - mos John saw it, In its grand-eur he saw it un - fold; And he saw that its walls were of jas - per, This beau - ti - ful cit - y of gold.

3. O they need not the sun in that cit - y, For the glo - ry of God, we are told, Is the light of that won - der - ful cit - y, The beau - ti - ful cit - y of gold.

4. I ex - pect to live there in that cit - y While the years of e - ter - ni - ty roll; I ex - pect to live there with my Sav - ior In the beau - ti - ful cit - y of gold.

CHORUS

I long for that cit - y, that cit - y, Its walls are of jas - per I'm told; I'm bound for that cit - y, That beau - ti - ful cit - y of gold.

I long for that cit - y, that cit - y so rare, I am told; I'm bound for that cit - y, that cit - y so fair,

Stand By Me

C. A. Tindley.
Arr. By F. A. Clark

1. When the storms of life are rag-ing, Stand by me; (stand by me;) When the
2. In the midst of trib-u-lat-tions,
3. In the midst of faults and failures,
4. In the midst of per-se-cu-tion,
5. When I'm grow-ing old and fee-ble,

(by me;) When I'm

storms of life are rag-ing, Stand by me;................... When the
midst of trib-u-la-tions,
midst of faults and fail-ures,
midst of per-se-cu-tion,
grow-ing old and fee-ble,

stand by me; When my

In the
In the
In the
When I'm

When the
When the
When I
When my

world is toss-ing me Like a ship up-on the sea;
hosts of hell as-sail, And my strength be-gins to fail,
do the best I can, And my friends mis-un-der-stand,
foes in bat-tle ar-ray Un-der-take to stop my way,
life be-comes a bur-den, And I'm near-ing chil-ly Jor-dan,

Thou who rul-est wind and wa-ter, Stand by me. (stand by me.)
Thou who nev-er lost a bat-tle,
Thou who know-est all a-bout me,
Thou who saved Paul and Si-las,
O thou "Lil-y of the Val-ley," (by me.)

No. 18 At Sunset I'm Going Home

Rev. Johnson Oatman, Jr. Copyright, 1927, by V. O. Stamps **Virgil O. Stamps**

Not too fast

1. Just a lit-tle while to tar-ry in this vale of grief and tears,
2. How I love to watch the bright stars blaz-ing in the midnight sky,
3. When I see the sun at ev-'ning flam-ing up the ros-y west,

Just a few more wea-ry, wea-ry miles to roam;.............
How they gleam and glit-ter in yon span-gled dome;.............
Light-ing like a beam of gold the o-cean's foam;.............

Then I'm go-ing to that country where they count not time by years, For at
Then I think of that bright mansion I'll in-hab-it by and by, For at
I shall look up-on that mo-ment as the one su-preme-ly blest, For at

REFRAIN

sun-set I'm go-ing, go-ing home. Won-der-ful the sun-set, mar-ve-lous the
                                Sun - set, sun -

sun-set, my sun soon may set, How it gilds with gol-den glo-ry heaven's
set,   How   it   gilds heav'n's

At Sunset I'm Going Home

vault - ed dome;   I am filled with singing, joy-bells now are ringing,
fair and vault-ed dome;   Sun - set, sun - set,

I shall nev - er fret, For at sun - set I'm go - ing, go - ing home.

No. 19   Help Me to Find the Way

Thos. Ramsey
Good as Solo

Thomas Ramsey, owner,

Thomas Ramsey

1. Sorrow's dark clouds gather o'er me, My heart is burdened with care;
2. All of my life has been wasted, Noth-ing to of - fer have I;
3. I would a - bide with Thee ev - er, Guide me, O Mas-ter, I pray;

FINE CHORUS

Humbly I bow now before Thee, O Lord, please hear my pray'r.
Life's bitter cup I have tast ed, Sav-ior, don't pass me by. Troubles have
That I shall stray from Thee never, Help me to find the way.

D. S.—*load, Lord, Help me to find the way.*

D. S.

roughened my road, Lord, Anguish o'er-shadows my way; Let Thy love lighten my

No. 20 Kneel At the Cross

Theme suggested by Rev. Sam. Hair

C. E. M.

Moody and Sebren, owners, 1924

Chas. E. Moody

1. Kneel at the cross, Christ will meet you there, Come while He waits for you;
2. Kneel at the cross, There is room for all Who would His glo - ry share;
3. Kneel at the cross, Give your i - dols up, Look un - to realms a - bove,

List to His voice, Leave with Him your care And be - gin life a - new.
Bliss there a - waits, Harm can ne'er be - fall Those who are anchored there.
Turn not a - way To life's sparkling cup, Trust on - ly in His love.

CHORUS.

Kneel............ at the cross,............ Leave............
Kneel at the cross, Kneel at the cross, Leave ev - 'ry care,

ev - 'ry care;............... Kneel.............. at the
Leave ev - 'ry care; Kneel at the cross,

cross,............ Je - sus will meet you there..............
Kneel at the cross, meet you there.

No. 21 Stay Beside Me Blessed Savior

C. G.　　　　　　　　　　　　　　　　　　　　　　Claude Goodman

1. O my pre-cious, lov-ing Sav-ior, Lend to me a help-ing
2. Leave me never, O dear Master, For with-out Thee I would
3. Time is short and days are fleeting And I have not long to
4. In this world my stay is transient, Death's dark vale I soon must

hand; May I ev-er do my du-ty, Help me,
stray; I'm so glad to know my Sav-ior Will go
stay, But I'll do my best for Je-sus As I
tread; With my Sav-ior close beside me, Naught have

CHORUS

Lord, to firm-ly stand. Stay be-side me O my
with me all the way.
go a-long life's way.
I to fear or dread. Stay be-side me bless-ed

stay beside me, Help me, Lord, to firmly stand;
Sav-ior, Help me, Lord, to firm-ly stand; When my

When my toil and strife is end-ed, Lead me to
toil and strife is end-ed, Lead me to the promised land.

You Gotta Live Your Religion Every Day

(SPIRITUAL)

: S. B. Clark   Copyright, 1933, by V. O. Stamps
1st and Chorus by V. O. S.   Virgil O. Stamps

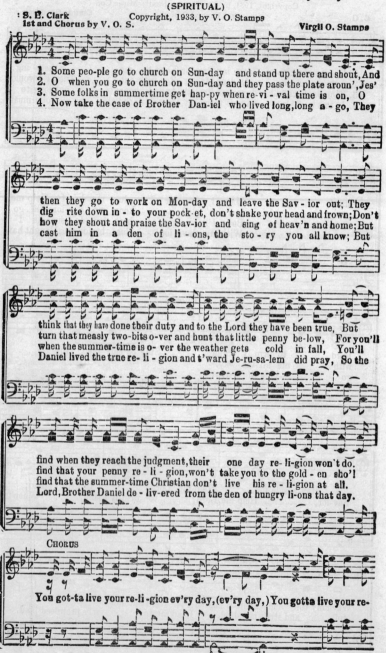

1. Some peo-ple go to church on Sun-day and stand up there and shout, And
2. O when you go to church on Sun-day and they pass the plate aroun', Jes'
3. Some folks in summertime get hap-py when re-vi-val time is on, O
4. Now take the case of Brother Dan-iel who lived long, long a-go, They

then they go to work on Mon-day and leave the Sav-ior out; They
dig rite down in-to your pock-et, don't shake your head and frown; Don't
how they shout and praise the Sav-ior and sing of heav'n and home; But
cast him in a den of li-ons, the sto-ry you all know; But

think that they have done their duty and to the Lord they have been true, But
turn that measly two-bits o-ver and hunt that little penny be-low, For you'll
when the summer-time is o-ver the weather gets cold in fall, You'll
Daniel lived the true re-li-gion and t'ward Je-ru-sa-lem did pray, So the

find when they reach the judgment, their one day re-li-gion won't do.
find that your penny re-li-gion, won't take you to the gold-en sho'!
find that the summer-time Christian don't live his re-li-gion at all.
Lord, Brother Daniel de-liv-ered from the den of hungry li-ons that day.

CHORUS

You got-ta live your re-li-gion ev'ry day, (ev'ry day,) You gotta live your re-

You Gotta Live Your Religion Every Day

li-gion ev'ry day; (ev'ry day;) On Monday, Tuesday, Wednesday, Thursday, Friday,

Sat-ur-day, Sunday, You gotta live your re - li-gion ev'-ry day. (ev'ry day.)

No. 23   They Scandalized my Name

(Mixed Quartet)

Arr. V. O. S.   Arr. copyright, 1930, by V. O. Stamps   Arr. by Virgil O. Stamps

I met a (sis-ter / brother / preacher / dea-con) the other day, I gave (her / him) my right hand And just as
Hum......................

soon   as   ev-er my back was turned (she / he) scandalized my name.
Just as soon as   Hum......................

CHORUS   1   2   **FINE**

Call that religion? No! No! Call that religion? No! No!   my name.
(Omit.... ....) Scandalized my name.

No. 24 There's A Rainbow Of Love In The Sky

J. R. Baxter, Jr.

Travis Bottoms
Denton McCoslin

1. There's a rain-bow of love that is pointing a - bove, Waving its ban-ner high;
2. Tho the path-way is rough and you meet with rebuff, Ma - ny may pass you by;
3. When our reaping is done, comes the setting of sun, Nev - er a - gain to sigh;

Let us fol-low the way it is lead-ing to - day, There's a rainbow of love
But re - mem-ber my friend, when the journey shall end,
We shall sweep thru the gate of that hap - py e - state,

in the sky.............. There's a rain-bow of love
that is shin - ing in the sky.
that is pointing a-bove,

CHORUS

Look ye wea - ry and lone and sad; .... O this glo - ry is sweet

Precious rainbow of promise that is mak-ing us glad.
bring-ing rapture complete,

No. 25 I'll Be List'ning

Arr. by V. O. STAMPS

1. When the Sav-ior calls I will an - swer, When He calls for me I will hear; When the Sav-ior calls I will an - swer, I'll be somewhere list'ning for my name.

2. If my heart is right when He calls me, If my heart is right I will hear; If my heart is right when He calls me, I'll be somewhere list'ning for my name.

3. If my robe is white when He calls me, If my robe is white I will hear; If my robe is white when He calls me, I'll be somewhere list'ning for my name.

CHORUS

I'll be somewhere list'ning, I'll be somewhere list'ning, I'll be somewhere list'ning for my name; yes, for my name; I'll be somewhere list'ning, I'll be somewhere list'ning, I'll be somewhere list'ning for my name.

Sweetest Mother

Gertrude Stoddard Dennstedt   Will M. Ramsey

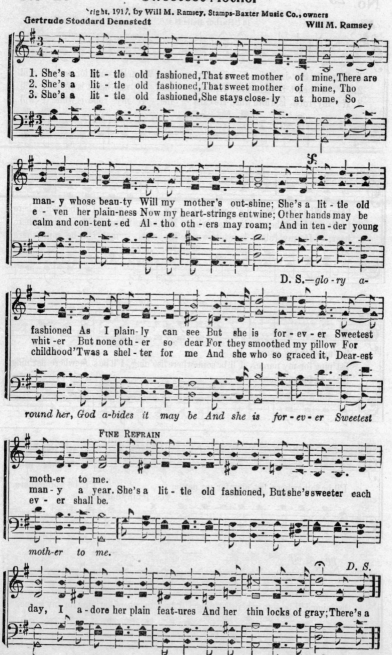

1. She's a lit-tle old fashioned, That sweet mother of mine, There are
2. She's a lit-tle old fashioned, That sweet mother of mine, Tho
3. She's a lit-tle old fashioned, She stays close-ly at home, So

man-y whose beau-ty Will my mother's out-shine; She's a lit-tle old
e-ven her plain-ness Now my heart-strings entwine; Other hands may be
calm and con-tent-ed Al-tho oth-ers may roam; And in ten-der young

D. S.—glo-ry a-

fashioned As I plain-ly can see But she is for-ev-er Sweetest
whit-er But none oth-er so dear For they smoothed my pillow For
childhood 'Twas a shel-ter for me And she who so graced it, Dear-est

round her, God a-bides it may be And she is for-ev-er Sweetest

FINE REFRAIN

moth-er to me. She's a lit-tle old fashioned, But she's sweeter each
man-y a year.
ev-er shall be.

moth-er to me.

D. S.

day, I a-dore her plain feat-ures And her thin locks of gray; There's a

O Mother, How We Miss You

Dedicated to Mrs. Roy Post, Topelo, Miss.

W. A. McKinney

E. M. Kitchen, owner,

E. M. Kitchen

1 We have lost our dear, sweet mother, She no more on earth shall
2 Moth-er's life was true and faith-ful And her heart was filled with
3 Some day I shall go to meet her Where there'll be no more good-

roam; And there'll nev-er be an-oth-er,...... Who can take her
love, Trusting Je - sus as her Sav-ior,...... Till she joined Him
byes, I can think of noth-ing sweet-er...... Than our meet - ing

CHORUS

place at home. O dear moth - - er, how we miss you,............
up a - bove.
in the skies. O dear mother, how we miss you,

But no more ..... on earth you roam; Some sweet day .. we'll all be
But no more on earth you roam; Some sweet day

Rit.

with you. .... In that bright...... e - ter-nal home.
we'll be with you In that bright sweet home.

No. 28   My Dream of Mother

Mrs. R. L. Wall   Virgil O. Stamps

1. I dreamed I saw moth-er in heav-en, An an-gel so bright and so fair,.... As she sang in the bright courts of glo-ry, And walked in the man-sions up there;.. The face I had loved so in child-hood, 'Tis dear-er than life now to me,.. I pray to the Lord, I shall meet her, And there with her ev-er shall be.....

2. I dreamed I saw moth-er up yon-der, In gar-ments so pure and so white,.. As she wandered thru gates of the cit-y, Where nev-er comes shades of the night;.. It seemed to me that she was search-ing The heav-en-ly por-tals a-bove,. Just look-ing and waiting my com-ing, With dear ones she once learned to love...

3. I dreamed I saw moth-er in heav-en, She sang man-y old songs to me,.... O the ones I once cherished so fond-ly, No songs ev-er sweet-er could be;.... She sang of the Sav-ior's sal-va-tion, And bade us to kneel at His feet,.. Ac-cept the great pardon He gives us, And life as my dream will be sweet..

CHORUS

I dreamed mother sang me to

My Dream of Mother

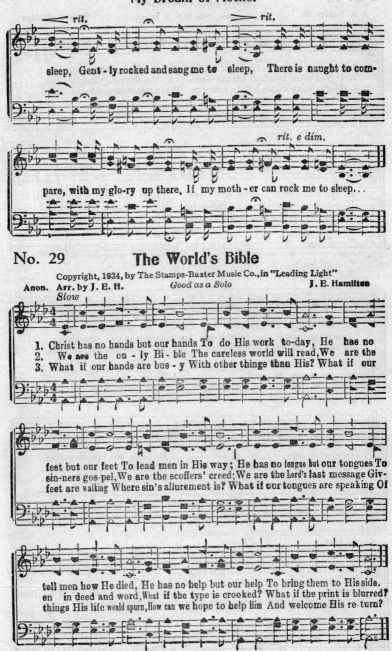

rit.   *rit.*

sleep, Gent-ly rocked and sang me to sleep, There is naught to com-

rit. e dim.

pare, with my glo-ry up there, If my moth-er can rock me to sleep...

Copyright, 1934, by The Stamps-Baxter Music Co., in "Leading Light"

No. 29   The World's Bible

Anon. Arr. by J. E. H.   *Good as a Solo*   J. E. Hamilton

Slow

1. Christ has no hands but our hands To do His work to-day, He has no
2. We are the on-ly Bi-ble The careless world will read, We are the
3. What if our hands are bus-y With other things than His? What if our

feet but our feet To lead men in His way; He has no tongue but our tongues To
sin-ners gos-pel, We are the scoffers' creed; We are the Lord's last message Giv-
feet are walking Where sin's allurement is? What if our tongues are speaking Of

tell men how He died, He has no help but our help To bring them to His side.
en in deed and word, What if the type is crooked? What if the print is blurred?
things His life would spurn, How can we hope to help Him And welcome His re-turn?

Like the Rainbow

J. R. Baxter, Jr.

Virgil O. Stamps

1. If you would make the world brighter   As o'er life's pathway you tread,
2. If you would help bear the bur-dens   Of the tired pilgrims be - low,
3. If you want friends here to miss you   When you cross o-ver the tide,

If you would drive a - way sor - row,   Hap-pi - ness 'round you spread;
If you would ban-ish their heart-aches,   Make their path brightly glow;
If you want foot-prints be- hind you   Safe- ly their feet to guide;

You must be faithful and earn - est,   Look to the Sav-ior di - vine.
You must be read y to help them   See thru each e - vil de - sign,
You must be careful, my broth - er,   Lest you should waste precious time,

You must be true   in all you do,   Just like the rain-bow shine.
Show them the way, teach them to pray,   Just like the rain-bow shine.
Do- ing your best,   un- der each test,   Just like the rain-bow shine.

CHORUS

Troubles, ... bur-dens, ...   cheer those who pine;
Troubles to share, bur- dens to bear, Help cheer the souls who pine:........

Like the Rainbow

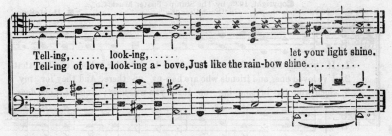

Tell-ing,...... look-ing,..... let your light shine.
Tell-ing of love, look-ing a - bove, Just like the rain-bow shine..........

No. 31 In Gethsemane Alone

S. E. R.   COPYRIGHT, 1912, BY THE TRIO MUSIC CO.   S. E. Reed.

1. Oh, what won-drous love I see Free - ly shown for you and me;
2. "Tar - ry here," He told the three, "Tar - ry here and watch with Me;"
3. Long in an - guish deep was He, Weep-ing there for you and me,

By the One who did a - tonel Pros-trate on His sa - cred face,
But they heard no bit - ter moan, For the three dis - ci - ples slept
For our sin to Him was known. We should love Him ev - er - more

D. S.—His for - ev - er I will be,
rit. FINE.

Je - sus suf - fered for the race, In Geth-sem - a - ne, a - lone.
While my lov - ing Sav - ior wept In Geth-sem - a - ne, a - lone.
For the an - guish that He bore In Geth-sem - a - ne, a - lone.

For the love He gave to me, When He suf - fered all a - lone.

REFRAIN. D.S.

Oh, what love, match-less love, Oh, what love.... for me was shown!
Oh, what love, match-less love, Oh, what love for me was shown!

Look for Me at the Gate

M. H. McKee

1. If you should reach heaven be-fore I ar-rive, And en-ter that
2. I've loved ones and friends who are hap-py up there, And they for my
3. Such won-der-ful sing-ing up there you will hear; And meet our dear

bless-ed es-tate,.. Re-mem-ber to meet you I'll ear-nest-ly strive,
com-ing a-wait;.. To join them and you I mean here to pre-pare,
Sav-ior so great;.. Be watch-ing for me as the cross-ing is near,

CHORUS

Just look for me at the gate.... Just look for me at the

gate,...... You'll not have long to a-wait;........ I'll sure-ly pre-pare
pearl-ly gate,   a-wait;

to meet you up there, Just look for me at the gate...........
                              beau-ti-ful gate.

We Are Climbing

Wilbur Wilson

1. We are climb-ing Jacob's gold en lad der From earth to heav-en so
2. Storms may gather, yet we keep on go ing From earth to heav-en so
3. Ev - 'ry mo-ment we are drawing near-er From earth to heav-en so

high,..........
This one tho't now makes my heart still gladder
Shin-ing rain-bows keep the love-light glowing
so ver-y high, hal-le-lu-jah, O what glad-ness, makes the Sav-ior dear-er

D. S. — I'm so hap-py as I jour-ney on-ward

We are climb-ing to the sky..........
To know that Ja-cob's lad-der up to the sky.

CHORUS
We are climb-ing still high-er up Ja-cob's bright lad-
Hal-le - lu - jah, hal-le - lu - jah, hal-le - lu-jah,

D. S.
der, Where we shall nev-er die;..........
hal-le - lu-jah, we'll nev-er die, hal-le - lu - jah;

No. 34 I Ain't A Gonna Let Satan Turn Me 'Roun'

SPIRITUAL

V. O. S.

Copyright, 1932, by V. O. Stamps

Virgil O. Stamps

1. I've left the land of E-gypt, I'm bound for Canaan's sho', I'm go-in' to a
2. Just take a tip from Lot's wife who started well, you know, The Lord had told them
3. The Lord told brother Jo-nah, a long, long time a-go, To go and preach and

lan' where milk an' hon-ey flow; When I cross o-ver Jor-dan, I
all to leave that place of woe; She turned and looked a-roun', a
pray in Nin-e-veh, you know; But he at once set sail, and

know I'll wear a crown, 'Cause I ain't a gon-na let Sa-tan turn me 'roun'.
pil-lar of salt was foun', 'Cause she went and let ol' Sa-tan turn her 'roun'.
landed in the belly of the whale, 'Cause he went and let ol' Sa-tan turn him 'roun'.

CHORUS

No, I ain't a gon-na let Sa-tan turn me 'roun',........ No, I
turn me 'roun',

ain't a gon-na let Sa-tan turn me 'roun'; I've start-ed to heav-en,

I Ain't A Gonna Let Satan Turn Me 'Roun'

I am glo-ry boun', And I ain't a gon-na let Sa-tan turn me 'roun'.

No. 35   When Jesus Was Dying for Me

Copyright, 1935, by The Stamps-Baxter Music Co., in "Thankful Hearts"

LUTHER G. PRESLEY   ROY W. PORTER

Slow

1. 'Tis sweet to re-mem-ber the love of my Lord Who suf-fered on dark Cal-va-
2. To think one so ho-ly could die in my stead, What love and com-pas-sion I
3. I think of the sor-row and pain that He bore, That day as He hung on the

ry, Re-demp-tion, I know, was the price of His blood, When Je-sus was
see; In tones full of pit-y "'Tis fin-ished" He said, When Je-sus was
tree; And blush when I see the rough crown that He wore, When Je-sus was

D. S.—When Je-sus was

FINE CHORUS

dy-ing for me. Love, love, such wonderful love, Love,
O won-der-ful, won-der-ful love,........ Compassion so

dy-ing for me.

D. S.

love, so full and so free; No wonder the sun failed to shine from a-bove,
full and so free;........

No. 36 Walking at my Side

James Rowe

C. Goodman
Chas. E. Durham

1. I have naught to fear on my jour-ney here, What-so-ev - er may be-
2. What-so-e'er the road to the true a-bode, Oft - en tho' I may be
3. Praise and bless His name, ev'ry day the same, All my needs He has sup-

tide; what-e'er be - tide;) For from day to day as I go my way
tried, (I oft am tried;) I shall nev - er roam from the cross-road home
plied; (my needs supplied;) For I know that He till the end will be

REFRAIN

I've a helper   walk-ing at my side. It is
For the Lord is
Ev - er near and al-ways walk-ing, walk-ing at   my   side. It is

Je - sus, bless - ed   Je - sus at my side, My Re-deem - er,
Je-sus, blessed Je-sus at my side, ... My Re-deemer, blessed

bless - ed   Sav - ior, friend and guide;
Savior, friend and guide; . . . .   Tri - als great be - fall, but He

helps thru all, For my Lord is al-ways walking, walking at my side.

walking at my side.

No. 37 I'll Be Satisfied.

Joe H. Pannell

T. N. Pannell, Owner, By per.

T. N. Pannell

1. When my soul is sing-ing In that promised land a - bove,
2. Liv-ing in a cit - y Where the soul shall nev - er die,
3. When I meet the ransomed O - ver on the gol - den shore,

I'll be sat - is - fied;

Prais-ing Christ the Sav-ior For re-
There to meet with loved ones, Never-
There I'll join the an-gels Sing-ing

D. S. When my soul is rest-ing In the

FINE.

deeming grace and love,
more to say good-by,
prais-es ev - er more.

I'll be sat - is - fied. I'll be sat - is-

pres-ence of the Lord. I'll be sat-is-fied.

D. S.

fied, sat - is - fied, I'll be sat - is - fied; sat - is - fied;

No. 38 When It's Sleepy Time in Heaven for Me

THOMAS RAMSEY Sug. by J. B. C.

J. B. COATS

1. O the shad-ows of the eve-ning were fall-ing And the sun had sunk
2. Moth-er gazed up-on her ba-by a mo-ment, As she whispered a

in the west, When a tired lit-tle boy came to moth-er To be
thank-ful pray'r, Ten-der-ly in her arms then she held him, Gent-ly

fon-dled and lulled to rest; She had told him a sto-ry of heav-en,
strok-ing his tou-sled hair; "Yes, my dar-ling, when you are in glo-ry,

As he knelt down be-side his bed, Then he slow-ly looked up to his
I am sure you can do all this, 'Cause the Sav-ior loves good lit-tle

CHORUS

moth-er, With a smile, these words the lad-die then said:
chil-dren, For of such is heav-en's king-dom of bliss." "When it's

When It's Sleepy Time in Heaven for Me

"Sleep-y time up there in heav-en a - bove, Will you rock me
sleep - y time for me up in heav-en,...... Will you still rock me to sleep on

to sleep on your breast? Sweet lull - a - by sung by an-gels in love,
your breast?...... Will a lull - a - by be sung by the an-gels,.... As I'm

Car-ried to dreamland of sleep and rest? Can I say pray'rs to the
car-ried to dreamland and rest?.... Can I say my lit-tle pray'rs to the

Sav-ior so fair, There by my bed up - on my knee? If I
Sav-ior...... As I bow by my bed on my knee?.... If they let me

do this I'll be hap-py up there, When it's sleepy time in heaven for me."
do these things I'll be happy,....

No. 39 There Will be no Disappointments

Mrs. Rilla Evans in "Leading Light" **Virgil O. Stamps**

DUET *Slow*

1. We will meet with dis - ap - point-ments As we jour-ney far and near, Of - ten we will be dis - cour-aged By some gos - sip that we hear; When a friend or dear com-pan - ion Fails to stand the slight-est test, Then the heart is filled with sor-row And the mind is sore op - pressed.

2. We should meet our dis - ap - point-ments With a brave and cheer-ful smile, Nev - er doubt the love of Je - sus, Skies will bright-en af - ter while; For the time is sure - ly com - ing When He'll roll the clouds a - way And our hearts will be re - joic-ing On the dawn-ing of that day.

3. There will be no dis - ap - point-ments And no tears where Je - sus is, There is peace and joy e - ter - nal In that home for all of His; We shall have no great temp-ta - tions, All our tri - als will be o'er, Joy be-yond our ex - pec - ta-tions On that fair and sin - less shore.

CHORUS *Faster*

Be no dis-appointments, dis-ap There will be no dis - ap - pointments

There Will be no Disappointments

pointments, Home a - cross the deep and mys - tic sea, Je - sus
In that home a - cross the sea,.............................

Made it all so per-fect, all so perfect, Yes, for you and
made it all so per-fect, Beau-ti - ful for you and

DUET *Slow*

beau - ti - ful for me; Sin and e - vil can-not grieve us, Friends and
me;.................

a tempo

loved ones will not leave us, Be no dis - ap-
There will be no dis - ap-

pointments, disappointments, All e - ter - ni - ty, e - ter - ni - ty.
pointments, Thru-out all e - ter - ni - ty.............

HE WILL BE WITH ME

James Rowe

Virgil O. Stamps

1. Who-so-ev-er may be be-fore me In the wea-ri-some gos-pel way; Whether black-ness or blue be o'er me, While work-ing for Him each day; I shall still be in His dear keep-ing, In His love will my spir-it be; So I'll still car-ry on the reap-ing, For my Sav-iour will be with me.

2. Ma-ny tri-als I shall be bear-ing, Ere I come to the pear-ly gate, But the Sav-iour for me is car-ing, Till mine are the joys that wait; I am sure He will nev-er leave me, And from sin He will keep me free; So I fear not what things may grieve me, For my Sav-iour will be with me.

3. Soon will end all my earth-ly sto-ry, Soon my tri-als will all be past, Then a-bove I shall share His glo-ry, And look on His face at last. So I rest in His bless-ed keep-ing, And I trust where I can-not see, And shall trust till I end the reap-ing, For my Sav-iour will be with me.

HE WILL BE WITH ME

Chorus *Alto prominent*

He will be with my soul ev-'ry hour of the
He will be near, near to my soul each min-ute and hour and

day,.......... He will keep me His own ev-'ry
all of the day, Oh, He will keep, keep me His own each

step of the way;.......... 'Till at heav- -en's bright
step of the way, each step of the way; 'Till at the gate,

gate His dear face I shall see,.......... I
heav-en's bright gate the face of my Lord and King I shall see,

f *ff*

know my Re-deem- -er will be with me.
Sure-ly I know Je-sus, my Friend, will ev-er be walk-ing with me.

No. 41   TELL HIM NOW

(FOR HE CANNOT READ HIS TOMBSTONE WHEN HE'S DEAD.)

Anon.   Arr. by V. O. S.   Virgil O. Stamps

1. If with pleas-ure you are view-ing An-y work a man is
2. Makes no diff'rence how you shout it, He won't real-ly care a-
3. More than fame and more than mon-ey, Is the com-ment kind and
4. If he earns your praise, be-stow it, If you like him, let him

do-ing, If you like him or you love him, tell him now;
bout it, He won't know how ma-ny tear-drops you have shed;
sun-ny, And the heart-y, warm ap-prov-al of a friend;
know it, And let words of true en-cour-age-ment be said;

Don't with-hold your ap-pro-ba-tion Till the par-son makes o-
If you think some praise is due him, Now's the time to give it
For it gives to life a sav-or, And it makes you strong-er,
Do not wait 'till life is o-ver, And he's un-der-neath the

ra-tion, And he lies with snow-y lil-ies o'er his brow.
to him, For he can-not read his tomb-stone when he's dead.
brav-er, And it gives you heart and spir-it to the end.
clov-er, For he can-not read his tomb-stone when he's dead.

TELL HIM NOW

Tell him now,........ Don't neg-lect to tell him, tell him now,
right now, to tell him now, ...

Place your hand in ap-pro-ba-tion on his head,............. Tell him
on his head,

now;........ Don't for-get to tell him, tell him now,
right now; to tell him now,....................

For he can-not read his tomb-stone when he's dead.................
when he's dead.

Coda

When he's dead, when he's dead, No, he can-not read his tomb-stone when he's dead.
when he's dead.

No. 42 — What Would You Give in Exchange

Copyright, 1912, by The Trio Music Co.

F. J. BERRY

J. H. CARR.

1. Broth-er a - far from the Sav-ior to - day, Risk-ing your soul for the
2. Mer - cy is call-ing you, won't you give heed? Must the dear Savior still
3. More than the sil - ver and gold of the earth,—More than all jew-els thy
4. If, when you stand at the bar by and by, When you are weighed in the

things that de - cay, Oh, if to - day God should call it a - way,
ten - der - ly plead? Risk not your soul, it is pre-cious in - deed:
spir - it is worth! God, the Cre - a - tor, has giv - en it birth!
bal - ance on high, You should be sentenced for - ev - er to die!

Fine. CHORUS.

What would you give in exchange for your soul? What would you give?

in exchange?

D. S.—*What would you give in exchange for your soul?*

What would you give? What would you give in ex-

in ex - change?

D. S.

change for your soul? Oh, if to - day God should call it a - way,

No. 43   The Lord Is My Shepherd.

H. W. Elliott.
Arr. by F. L. E.

H. W. Elliott.
ASr. by J. E. T.

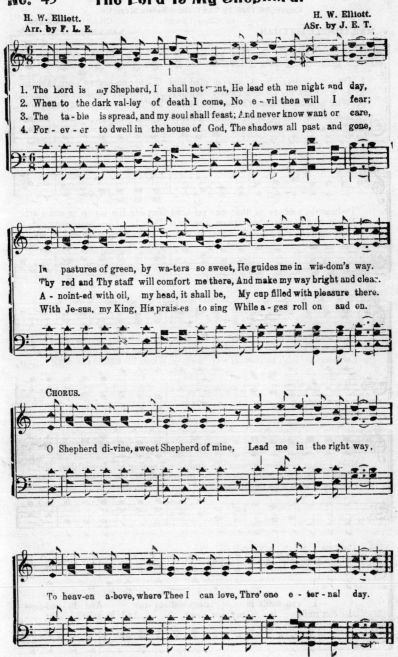

1. The Lord is my Shepherd, I shall not want, He lead eth me night and day,
2. When to the dark val-ley of death I come, No e - vil then will I fear;
3. The ta - ble is spread, and my soul shall feast; And never know want or care,
4. For - ev - er to dwell in the house of God, The shadows all past and gone,

In pastures of green, by wa-ters so sweet, He guides me in wis-dom's way.
Thy red and Thy staff will comfort me there, And make my way bright and clear.
A - noint-ed with oil, my head, it shall be, My cup filled with pleasure there.
With Je-sus, my King, His prais-es to sing While a - ges roll on and on.

CHORUS.

O Shepherd di-vine, sweet Shepherd of mine, Lead me in the right way,

To heav-en a-bove, where Thee I can love, Thro' one e - ter - nal day.

No. 44   The Land of My Dreams

MRS. LOWELL PITTMAN   CHARLINE CRAIG
EARNEST RIPPETOE

1. Oft - en in dreaming I see a glad land O - ver on heaven's bright shore.
2. I want my life to show clearly each day, Je - sus is liv - ing in me,
3. With hope and gladness a-bid-ing with-in, Flow'rs on my path-way will grow,

I hear the voic - es of that an - gel band Sing-ing His love o'er and o'er;
Brighter and brighter to shine on the way That I of ser-vice may be;
Help-ing me for the dear Sav-ior to win, E - ven when shadows are low;

Then with new vis-ion I look on His face, Having such gladness com-plete,
I want to know that each mile that I tread, Here on this trouble-some road,
Look-ing by faith to that ci - ty a -bove, Where the bright mansion now gleams,

Noth-ing but rap-ture my soul to embrace, Kneeling at Je-sus' dear feet.
Christ is be-side me to les-sen my dread, Help-ing me car-ry my load.
Dai - ly I walk with this Friend that I love On to the land of my dreams.

CHORUS

I can smile in   deep - est sor - row   And in sad-ness
I can smile in   my sor - row,....   And in grief   not

The Land of My Dreams

No. 45   I Am Going

J. R. Baxter, Jr.   Virgil O. Stamps

1. I am go-ing up to heav-en fair When my pil-grim-age on
2. I am go-ing up to glo-ry-land There to wear a robe so
3. I am go-ing to an end-less home, Don't you want to go a-

earth is o'er, And I know I'll meet my loved ones there, When I
pure and white, And I want to hold my Sav-ior's hand, In that
long with me? There no more my feet shall ev-er roam, Thru the

reach that hap-py gold-en shore; But best (but best) of all (of all) the
cit-y where there is no night; No winds (no winds) to blow (to blow) and
a-ges of e-ter-ni-ty; And you (and you) may have (may have) His

Lamb who died for me. His love to show, will wel-come me, I know,
fill my soul with fear, So glad and free, how hap-py I shall be,
love your soul to thrill, He calls for you, His prom-is-es are true,

CHORUS

When His smil-ing face I see.   I am
Liv-ing with my Sav-ior dear.
One is "who-so-ev-er will."   I am go-ing o-ver

I Am Going

No. 46   Satisfied

Anna B. Steinhoff   I. W. C. Arr. by J. L. Moore

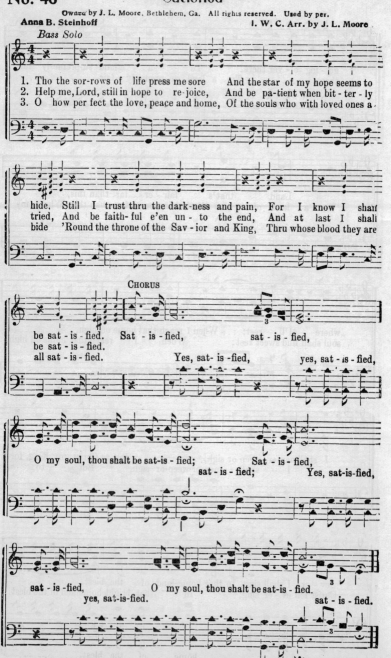

1. Tho the sor-rows of life press me sore And the star of my hope seems to
2. Help me, Lord, still in hope to re-joice, And be pa-tient when bit-ter-ly
3. O how per-fect the love, peace and home, Of the souls who with loved ones a-

hide, Still I trust thru the dark-ness and pain, For I know I shall
tried, And be faith-ful e'en un-to the end, And at last I shall
bide 'Round the throne of the Sav-ior and King, Thru whose blood they are

Chorus

be sat-is-fied.   Sat-is-fied,   sat-is-fied,
be sat-is-fied.
all sat-is-fied.   Yes, sat-is-fied,   yes, sat-is-fied,

O my soul, thou shalt be sat-is-fied;   Sat-is-fied,
sat-is-fied;   Yes, sat-is-fied,

sat-is-fied,   O my soul, thou shalt be sat-is-fied.
yes, sat-is-fied.   sat-is-fied.

After the Sunrise

J. R. Baxter, Jr. Sug. by E. W. in "Leading Light"   Eugene Wright

1. Sor-rows surround us while treading life's road, Troubles confound us, make
2. Shadows will van-ish when morning shall come, Lovelight will ban-ish sin's
3. An - gels are wait-ing to car - ry the news, Why stand de-bat-ing, why

heav - y our load; Fetters that bound us, no long-er will goad, Af - ter the
va - pors like scum; Ev - en the clan-ish to - geth-er will hum, Af - ter the
lon - ger re - fuse? Cease all your hateing, be changing your views, Af - ter the

CHORUS

sun-rise, how hap - py we'll be.   hap - py we'll be,
Af - ter the sun-rise,

Je - sus we'll see;   All will be
We know af - ter the sun-rise,   in heav-en;

glo - ry, singing the sto - ry, Af-ter the sun-rise, how hap-py we'll be.

No. 48 He Whispers Sweet Peace to Me

W. M. R.

WILL M. RAMSEY

1. Some-time when mis-giv-ings dark-en the day, And faith's light I can-not see; I ask my dear Lord to bright-en the way, He whis-pers sweet peace to me.
2. I could not go on with-out Him I know, The world would o'er whelm my soul; For I could not see the right way to go, When temp-ta-tions o'er me roll.
3. I trust Him through faith, by faith hold His hand, And sometimes my faith is weak, And then when I ask Him to take com-mand, It seems that I hear Him speak.
4. He speaks in a still, small voice we are told, A voice that dis-pels all fear; And when I'm in doubt, or trou-bled in soul, That still small voice I can hear.

REFRAIN

He whis-pers sweet peace to me,......... He whis-pers sweet peace to me,......... When I am cast down in spir-it and soul, He whispers sweet peace to me.

Yes He whis-pers to me, He whis-pers sweet peace to me,

Skies Will Smile Again

James Rowe

R. H. Cornelius, owner

R. H. Cornelius

1. Life is drear-y, you are weary, Teardrops fall
2. Troubles bearing; you're despairing, Life seems all
3. Loved ones grieve you, slight and leave you, Still let hope
4. Clouds will vanish, clouds shall banish, What should not

like rain; But to-mor-row heart of sor-row;
in vain; Yet with morning's bright re-turn-ing,
re-main, Trust your Savior, seek His fav - or,
re-main; Heart of sor-row on the mor-row

REFRAIN *Softer and faster*

Skies will smile a-gain. Look to Je - sus, love and
trust Him, Smile a-way your pain; He is near you
and will cheer you; Skies will smile......... .... will smile a - gain.

No. 50 Launch Out on the Sea of God's Love

Rev. B. B. Edmiaston   Copyright, 1930, by V. O. Stamps   Virgil O. Stamps

1. Dear friend, are you trust-ing the Sav-ior to-day, Ac-cept-ing His
2. True faith in Him, tho' it is small, will re-move The mountains of
3. O trust not in self, but re-ly on the Lord, With heart set on

prom-is-es sweet; Is faith tak-ing hold of His word to o-bey,
doubt and of sin; By work-ing for Je-sus your faith you will prove,
things up a-bove; Be-liev-ing each prom-ise contained in His word,

CHORUS

In bless-ed as-sur-ance com-plete? Launch out to-day,
And, thru Him, the vic-to-ry win.
Launch out on the sea of God's love. Launch out........ on the

out on the sea, On the sea of God's love,
sea,.......... Launch out on the sea of God's love,........ The

Faith of His saints, faith of His saints, Mountains will move,
faith .... of His saints, ... The moun - - tains will

Launch Out on the Sea of God's Love

mourtains will move; Launch out to-day, out on the sea,
move; ....Launch out.......... on the sea,.......... Launch

And God's prom-is-es prove, Doubt Him no more,
out and the prom-is-es prove,........ O doubt......... Him no

doubt Him no more, Launch out on the sea of God's love........ ..
more, ... out on the sea of God's love.

No. 51   He Knows

G. W. Lyon

With expression

1. He knows the bit-ter, wea-ry way, The end-less strivings day by day,
2. He knows how hard the fight has l·een, The clouds that come our lives between,
3. He knows when faint and worn we sink, How deep the pain, how near the brink
4. He knows! O tho't so full of bliss! For tho' on earth our joys we miss,

Hum..........

The souls that weep, the souls that pray, He knows, He knows.
The wounds the world has nev-er seen.
Of dark de-spair, we pause and shrink,
We still can bear it feel-ing this, He knows, He knows.

No. 52   It Won't Be Long

L. G. P.

Copyright, 1930, by The Stamps-Baxter Music Co.   **Luther G. Presley**

1. I'm walk-ing in the gos-pel way with my e-ter-nal Friend,
2. It won't be long till I shall reach the end-ing of the road
3. It won't be long till I shall stand up-on the gold-en shore

Up-on .... His love ..... I al-ways can de-pend, (de pend,)
And there .... I'll lay ..... a-side my heav-y load, (my load.)
With all ...... the saints .... my Sav-ior to a-dore, (a-dore,)

With Him I know that I shall reach the hap-py land of song,
Thru end-less a-ges I shall sing with all the ran-somed throng,
There in the New Je-ru-sa-lem O how we'll wake the song!

I'll soon be there, Praise the Lord it won't be long ....
I'll soon ..... be there ...... ver-y long.

CHORUS

It won't .... be long   Till with rap-ture I shall see ....
It won't be long   sure-ly see

It Won't Be Long

The One who free-ly died On the cross for me,
The One...... who died .... On the cru-el cross for me,

The One who died On the cross for me,....

It won't.... be long Now for me to wait,
It won't be long, not ver-y long Now for me to watch and wait,

It won't.... be long Now for me to wait,

Just a few more weary miles Till I reach the pearly gate....
Just a few weary miles Till I reach the pearly gate....
A few .... more miles Till I reach the pear-ly gate.

No. 53   Sleep, Little One, Sleep

J. H. S.   J. H. Stewart. owner.   J. H. Stewart

1. Sleep, thou lit - tle one, sleep, The Lord thy dear spir - it will keep:
2. Sleep, thou dar - ling one, sleep, While fa - ther and moth-er must weep;
3. Rest, thou pre-cious one, rest, So sweet-ly and peace-ful - ly rest;

Thou nev-er shall know of the woes here below, Sleep, thou little one, sleep.
While friends here must mourn because heart strings are torn, Sleep, thou darling one, sleep.
Thy soul shall awake and true pleasures partake, Rest, thou precious one, rest.

No. 54   Looking This Way

Arr. Copyright, 1936, by The Stamps-Baxter Music Co.
J. W. V.   J. W. Van De Venter
Arr. by J. R. BAXTER, JR.

1. O - ver the riv-er fa-ces I see, Fair as the morn-ing,
2. Fa - ther and moth-er, safe in the vale, Watch for the boat-man,
3. Broth-er and sis - ter, gone to that clime Wait-ing for oth-ers,
4. Sweet lit - tle dar - ling, light of the home, Look-ing for some-one,
5. Je - sus the Sav - ior, bright Morn-ing Star, Look-ing for lost ones,

look - ing for me; Free from their sor-row, grief and de-spair,
wait for the sail; Bear-ing the loved ones o - ver the tide,
com - ing some-time; Safe with the an - gels, whit - er than snow,
beck - on - ing come; Bright as a sun-beam, pure as the dew,
stray - ing a - far; Hear the glad mes-sage, why will you roam?

CHORUS

Wait-ing and watch-ing pa-tient - ly there. Look-ing this way,
In - to the har - bor near to their side.
Watching for dear ones wait-ing be-low. Look-ing this
Anx - ious - ly look-ing moth-er for you.
Je - sus is call-ing, "sin - ner, come home."

yes, look - ing this way, Loved ones are wait - - - ing,
way, yes, look - ing this way, Loved ones are wait-

look-ing this way; Fair as the morn - ing bright as the
ing look - ing this way; Fair as the morn-ing,

Looking This Way

day,　　　Dear ones in glo - ry look-ing this way.
bright as the day,　　　Dear ones in glo - ry　　look-ing this way.

No. 55　Daddy Has Gone

Copyright, 1934, by The Stamps-Baxter Music Co.
Theda Bird and Mrs. M. B. R.　　in "Leading Light"　　Mrs. Mildred Bird Ross

1. There is a ci-ty su-per-nal,　　God has prepared for His own;
2. Since you have left us, dear Daddy,　　Days are so drear-y and long;
3. Fa-ther has gone on to heav-en,　　Cir - cles are broken down here;

We read that it is e-ter-nal,　　That's where our loved one has gone.
We promised you we'd be read-y,　　When God says "children, come home."
Soon mother's pray'rs will be answered,　　We'll be to-geth-er up there.

CHORUS

Dad-dy you've gone to that ci-ty,　　Where there's no sorrow or care;

rit.

Sure-ly you know that we miss you,　　Some day we'll meet you up there.

ANCHORED IN LOVE DIVINE

Rearranged expressly for V. O. Stamps, by A. M. Pace.

James Rowe   Howard E. Smith

1. Fear-ing the storm no more,   Dread-ing no rock or shoal,
2. Bil - lows may swell and roll,   Fierce-ly the storm may beat,
3. Here I will rest with Him,   Je - sus my Sav-iour dear,

Hear-ing no breakers roar,   Peace-ful is now my soul.
Safe will remain my soul   Here in His ref - uge sweet,
Till thro' the shadows dim   Life's end-less morn ap-pear;

O - ver my wand'ring days   I shall no more re - pine;
All thro' the night I see   Homelights that brightly shine,
Then on the hap - py shore,   Where homes e-ter-nal shine,

rit.

Sing-ing to Je - sus a car-ol of praise, I'm anchored in love di - vine.
All will be well till the morning with me, I'm anchored in love di - vine.
Songs I shall sing in His praise ev-er-more, Still anchored in love di - vine.

Chorus

Anchored in love di - vine,   Je - sus at last is mine,

ANCHORED IN LOVE DIVINE

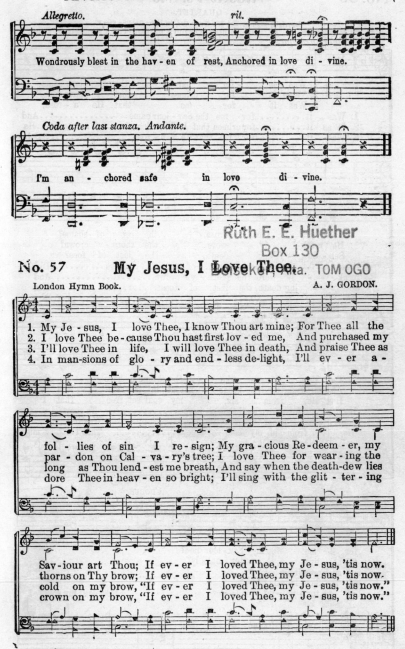

Allegretto.   *ril.*

Wondrously blest in the hav - en of rest, Anchored in love di - vine.

Coda after last stanza. Andante.

I'm an - chored safe in love di - vine.

No. 57   My Jesus, I Love Thee.

London Hymn Book.   A. J. GORDON.

1. My Je - sus, I love Thee, I know Thou art mine; For Thee all the
2. I love Thee be - cause Thou hast first lov - ed me, And purchased my
3. I'll love Thee in life, I will love Thee in death, And praise Thee as
4. In man-sions of glo - ry and end - less de-light, I'll ev - er a -

fol - lies of sin I re - sign; My gra - cious Re - deem - er, my
par - don on Cal - va - ry's tree; I love Thee for wear - ing the
long as Thou lend - est me breath, And say when the death-dew lies
dore Thee in heav - en so bright; I'll sing with the glit - ter - ing

Sav - iour art Thou; If ev - er I loved Thee, my Je - sus, 'tis now.
thorns on Thy brow; If ev - er I loved Thee, my Je - sus, 'tis now.
cold on my brow, "If ev - er I loved Thee, my Je - sus, 'tis now."
crown on my brow, "If ev - er I loved Thee, my Je - sus, 'tis now."

No. 58 Was It For Me?

QUARTET.

Copyright, 1917, by The Trio Music Co., in "The Guiding Star."
F. F. Pub. House, Owners of Copyright

B. B. Edmiaston. Emmett S. Dean.

Con espressione.

1. Was it for me the Sav-iour came
2. "Was it for crimes that I have done,"
3. Was it for me that He a-rose,

1. Was it........for me the Sav-iour came.................And
2. "Was it........for crimes that I have done,".................He
3. Was it........for me that He a-rose,.................Sub-

And bore the cross, the cross of shame?
He meek-ly wore the thorn-y crown?
Sub-du-ing death, the last of foes?

bore........the cross, the cross of shame?.................Did
meek--ly wore the thorn-y crown?.................And
du--ing death, the last of foes;.................Has

Did He for-sake the throne a-bove To show
And bore the spear-thrust in His side? Was it
Has He, from sin, my soul set free That I

He........for-sake the throne a-bove.............To show......for
bore........the spear-thrust in His side,.............Was it........for
He,........from sin, my soul set free.............That I........might

CHORUS.

for me such won-drous love? Re-joice, my soul, I
for me my Sav-iour died?
might live e-ter-nal-ly?

me such wondrous love?
me the Sav-iour died?
live e-ter-nal-ly? Re-joice, my soul, I

Was It For Me?

know it was for me...... the bless-ed Sav-iour came.... and
it was for me   the Sav-iour came,

bore the cross of shame;... While a - ges roll, from sin I shall be
the cross of shame;   While a - ges roll,   I

rit.

free,....... With rapt - ure I shall sing......and praise the conqu'ring King,
shall be free,   with rapt-ure sing

No. 59   Enough For Me.

E. A. H.   (arranged)   REV. E. A. HOFFMAN.

1. O love, sur - pass-ing know-ledge! O grace, so full and free!
2. O won - der - ful sal - va - tion! From sin He makes me free!
3. O blood of Christ, so pre - cious, Poured out on Cal - va - ry!

Cho.—And that's e - nough for me,   And that's e - nough for me,

I know that Je - sus saves me, And that's e - nough for me.
I feel the sweet as - sur - ance, And that's e - nough for me.
I feel its cleans-ing pow - er And that's e - nough for me.

I know that Je - sus saves me, And that's e - nough for me.
I feel the sweet as - sur - ance, And that's e - nough for me.
I feel its cleans-ing pow - er, And that's e - nough for me.

Years Roll On

B. B. Edmiaston   Robert E. Arnold

1. Our days on earth are numbered, swiftly they're passing away, How fleeting
2. No time is giv-en us to bar-ter or i-dle a-way, There's so much
3. The somber shad-ows of the ev-'ning will quick-ly appear, From old and

are the years of man;   The ros-y morn-ing quick-ly
work and years so few; (they're rolling on;) Our lives are pass-ing by, the
young the years roll on;   The Sav-ior's bless-ed wel-come

O the years are roll-ing on.
changes to golden noon-day, Then ev'ning shadows end the span............
Mas-ter is call-ing to-day, The warning comes to me and you............
plaudit the faithful shall hear, And ev'ry sor-row shall be gone............

Chorus

Years roll on,   years roll
Whether precious hours in sin you squander, or of better things your heart grows

on,   Years roll on, the years roll on;
fon-der, Records are in mak-ing o-ver yon-der, and

Years Roll On

Years roll on, years roll
Hear the bless-ed Sav-ior for you call-ing, lon-ger to re-ject Him is ap-

on, Years roll on, and the years roll on.
pall-ing, Shadows of the night are swiftly fall-ing,

No. 61 Love Found a Way for Me

J. R. B., Jr.   Copyright, 1927, by J. R. Baxter, Jr.   J. R. Baxter, Jr.

1. When I was lost in sin and disgrace, Love found a way for me;
2. Once I was bound by fet-ters of shame,
3. 'Twas all because my God loved me so, Won-der-ful love found a way for me;

D. S.   **FINE**

Now I can find in heav-en my place, Love found a way for me.
Now I am free, O praise His dear name,
Now I can sing as homeward I go, Won-der-ful love found a way for me.

D. S.-"Once I was blind but now I can see," Love found a way for me.

D. S.

CHORUS

Love found a way for me, Love found a way for me;
Won-der-ful love Won-der-ful love

Go To Jesus With It All

F. L. E.

Arr. Copyright, 1937, by The Stamps-Baxter Music Co.

F. L. EILAND

1. Is there heav-y weight of care, In thy bo-som an-y where,
2. In thy trou-ble He is near, Oh, my bro-ther, do not fear,
3. You can touch Him with your cry, And He'll nev-er pass you by,
4. When, Him trust-ing, you have tried, You'll be ful-ly sat-is fied,

And you need a friend to sym-pa-thize with you? Go to
Ask of Him the bur-den there to roll a-way, That His
For He feels the depths of all thy spir-it's woe, He has
That there is no oth-er friend like this dear one, He such

Je-sus with it all, And for com-fort on Him call, He will
spir-it en-ter in, And His might-y work be-gin, And thy
travel-ed sor-row's road And has car-ried of its load, And He'll
bless-ing will im-part, As will glad-den all thy heart, Go to

D. S.—He's a com-fort-er in-deed, Go to

FINE CHORUS

give you such, as oth-ers can-not do!
soul will have a hap-py, hap-py day! Go to Je-sus with it all,
car-ry thine, my bro-ther, to Him go!
Him if you would have it sure-ly done!

Je-sus with it all, with it all!

Go to Je-sus with it all, He's the help-er that you need,

Heaven Holds All To Me

T. S. T.

TILLIT S. TEDDLIE

Not too fast

1. Earth holds no treasures but perish with using, How-ev-er
2. Out on the hill of that won-der-ful coun-try, Hap-py, con-
3. Why should I long for the world and its sor-rows, When in that

pre-cious they be; Yet there's a coun-try to which I am
tent-ed and free, Loved ones are wait-ing and watching my
home o'er the sea, Mil-lions are sing-ing the won-der-ful

Chorus

go-ing, Heaven holds all to me.
com-ing, Heaven holds all to me. Heaven holds all to
sto-ry, Heaven holds all to me.

me,........ Brighter its glo-ry will be; Joy with-out
to me,

measure will be my treasure, Heaven holds all

No. 64 Jesus Calls For Workers.

PEARL H. FARMER.   Owned by J. M. Greer.   J. M. GREER.

1. The noon-day sun is shin - ing, All o - ver land and sea; The call for
2. You've often pray'd the Fa - ther To o - pen wide the door; To Thee 'tis
3. The call for will-ing work - ers Is ring-ing all a-round, At home and
4. A - wake, ye Christian sleepers! The hours are fly - ing fast. Waste not the

will-ing workers Come forth to you and me; O will you go, my broth-er, Be-
now thrown open; O haste, ere time's no more, For some one who is yearning, A
o'er the o - cean, Wher-ev-er man is found; How strange that we should idle, Make
precious moments, For time will soon be past. When you are called to judgment, How

fore the light grows dim? God calls you, too, my sis - ter, To lead some soul to Him.
bet - ter life to live; Go tell them Je-sus loves them, For them His life did give.
life a use-less dream, When souls of men are dy - ing, For Je-sus's love supreme.
ma - ny will have heard, From you, of Je-sus' pow - er, Told thro' His precious word.

Chorus.

He's calling you,   He's calling you In-to the fields of sin;
He's call-ing you, ...   He's calling you, ...

Make no delay,   but go to-day, And bring the lost ones in.
Make no de-lay, ...   but go to-day, ...

No. 65 If I Could Hear My Mother Pray Again

JAMES ROWE J. W. Vaughan, owner J. W. VAUGHAN

1. How sweet and hap-py seem those days of which I dream, When mem-o-
2. She used to pray that I on Je-sus would re-ly, And al-ways
3. With-in the old home-place, her pa-tient, smil-ing face, Was al-ways
4. Her work on earth is done, the life-crown has been won, And she will

ry re-calls them now and then! And with what rap-ture sweet my
walk the shin-ing gos-pel way; So trust-ing still His love I
spreading com-fort, hope and cheer; And when she used to sing to
be at rest with Him a-bove; And some glad morn-ing, she I

wea-ry heart would beat, If I could hear my mo-ther pray a-gain.
seek that home a-bove, Where I shall meet my mo-ther some glad day.
her e-ter-nal King, It was the songs the an-gels loved to hear.
know will welcome me To that e-ter-nal home of peace and love.

D. S.—so much to me, If I could hear my mo-ther pray a-gain.

Chorus

If I could hear my mo-ther pray a-gain, If I could
If I could on-ly If I could on-ly

If I could on-ly hear

hear her ten-der voice as then! So glad I'd be, t'would mean
hap-py I should

hap-py I should be

Tell Them of His Love

Thomas Ramsey   A. P. Wammack

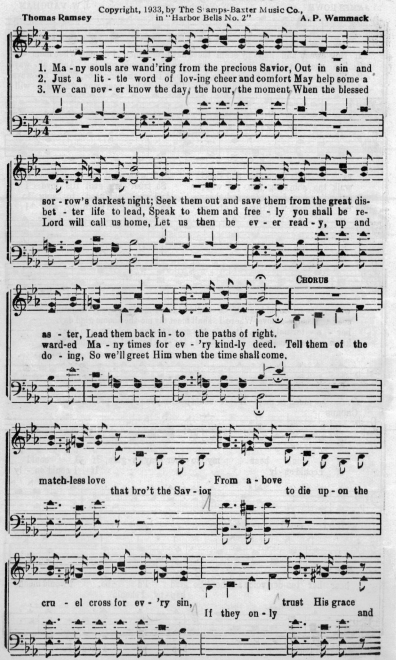

1. Ma-ny souls are wand'ring from the precious Savior, Out in sin and
2. Just a lit-tle word of lov-ing cheer and comfort May help some a
3. We can nev-er know the day, the hour, the moment When the blessed

sor-row's darkest night; Seek them out and save them from the great dis-
bet-ter life to lead, Speak to them and free-ly you shall be re-
Lord will call us home, Let us then be ev-er read-y, up and

CHORUS

as-ter, Lead them back in-to the paths of right.
ward-ed Ma-ny times for ev-'ry kind-ly deed. Tell them of the
do-ing, So we'll greet Him when the time shall come.

match-less love   that bro't the Sav-ior   From a-bove   to die up-on the

cru-el cross for ev-'ry sin,   If they on-ly   trust His grace   and

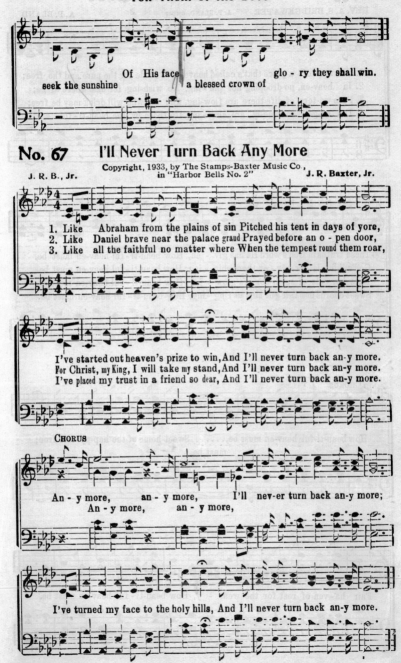

Tell Them of His Love

seek the sunshine Of His face a blessed crown of glo - ry they shall win.

No. 67 — I'll Never Turn Back Any More

Copyright, 1933, by The Stamps-Baxter Music Co.,
in "Harbor Bells No. 2"

J. R. B., Jr.   J. R. Baxter, Jr.

1. Like Abraham from the plains of sin Pitched his tent in days of yore,
2. Like Daniel brave near the palace grand Prayed before an o - pen door,
3. Like all the faithful no matter where When the tempest round them roar,

I've started out heaven's prize to win, And I'll never turn back an-y more.
For Christ, my King, I will take my stand, And I'll never turn back an-y more.
I've placed my trust in a friend so dear, And I'll never turn back an-y more.

CHORUS

An - y more,   an - y more,   I'll nev-er turn back an-y more;
An - y more,   an - y more,

I've turned my face to the holy hills, And I'll never turn back an-y more.

How Beautiful Heaven Must Be

REV. A. S. BRIDGEWATER   A. P. BLAND, owner   A. P. BLAND

1. We read of a place that's called heaven, It's made for the pure and the free;
2. In heav-en, no drooping nor pin-ing, No wish-ing for else where to be;
3. Pure wa-ters of life there are flow-ing, And all who will drink may be free;
4. The an-gels so swee-ly are sing-iug, Up there by the beau-ti-ful sea;

These truths in God's word He has giv - en, How beau-ti-ful heav-en must be.
God's light is for - ev - er there shin - ing, How beau-ti-ful heav-en must be.
Rare jew - els of splen-dor are glow - ing, How beau-ti-ful heav-en must be.
Sweet chords from their gold harps are ring - ing, How beau-ti-ful heav-en must be.

CHORUS

How beau-ti-ful heav-en must be,.......Sweet home of the hap-py and free;
                 must be,

Fair ha-ven of rest for the wear - y, How beau-ti-ful heav-en must be.

No. 69

I'll Make it my Home

Mrs. L. J. Morris   Copyright, 1930, by The Stamps-Baxter Music Co.   C. C. Stafford

1. I've heard of a beau-ti-ful cit-y a-bove, Where no one can go a-stray; And since I am trust-ing His won-der-ful love, I'll make it my home some day.
2. I've heard of a cit-y with streets of pure gold, Where treasures can not de-cay; Where love's blessed sto-ry with rap-ture is told, I'll make it my home some day.
3. I've heard of a cit-y where stands the great throne, And an-gels in white ar-ray Are prais-ing my Lord, with my loved and His own, I'll make it my home some day.
4. So pa-tient-ly, lov-ing-ly trust-ing my Lord, Till I shall be called a-way, I la-bor and wait, for I know His re-ward My soul shall en-joy some day.

REFRAIN

I'll make it my home some day,...... some day, When shad-ows have passed a-way; (a-way;) A man-sion of love is wait-ing a-bove, I'll make it my home some day.(some day.)

Give Them a Lift

E. W.

Eugene Wright

1. While go-ing on-ward thru life, with all its trou-ble and strife, You'll find man-y souls who've wan-dered far as-stray; Don't laugh and jeer at their plight, but lead them in-to the light, Just give them a lift, 'twill help them on their way.

2. We see lost souls in de-spair, and bur-dened heav-y with care, From shore they are drift-ing far-ther ev-'ry day; Don't turn deaf ears to their plea, tho' some may lep-er-ous be, Just give them a lift,

3. If we would live for the Lord and gain the hap-py re-ward, We'll stand for the right in all we do or say; So let us do what we can to be of serv-ice to man, Just give them a lift,

CHORUS

Give them a lift, Just give them a

Give Them a Lift

give them a lift, don't push them furth-er down, A
lift,

smile ___ an - y day ___ is bet - ter than a
Sun - ny lit - tle smile ___ an - y day
Sun - ny smile

frown; A pat on the back, a good word of cheer, will

light - en their load while trav - el - ing here, Give them a
Just give

lift, ___ give them a lift, 'twill help them on their way.
them a lift,

No. 71 As the Life of a Flower.

LAURA E. NEWELL.   G. H. RAMSEY.

1. As the life of a flow'r, As a breath or a sigh, So the years that we
2. As the life of a flow'r, Be our lives pure and sweet; May we brighten the
3. While we tar-ry be-low Let us trust and a-dore Him who leads us each

live As a dream has-ten by; True, to-day we are here, But to-
way For the friends that we greet; And sweet in-cense a-rise, From our
day Tow'rd the ra-di-ant shore Where the sun nev-er sets, And the

mor-row may see Just a grave in the vale, And a mem-'ry of me.
hearts as we live Close to Him who doth teach Us to love and for-give.
flow'rs nev-er fade, Where no sor-row or death May its bor-ders in-vade.

CHORUS.

As the life of a flow'r, As a
As the life of a flow'r,

breath, or a sigh, So the years
As a breath, or a sigh, So the years

As the Life of a Flower.

Repeat pp after last stanza.
Rit.

glide a - way,   And a - las,   we must die.

glide a - way,   And a - las,   we must die.

What Will Your Answer Be?

T. S. T.

Tillit S. Teddlie, owner, 1935

Tillit S. Teddlie

1. Some day you'll stand at the bar on high, Some day your record you'll see;
2. Sad - ly you'll stand, if you're unprepared, Trembling, you'll fall on your knee;
3. Now is the time to prepare, my friend, Make your soul spotless and free;

Some day you'll an-swer the question of life, What will your an-swer be?
Fac - ing the sentence of life or of death, What will that sentence be?
Washed in the blood of the Cru - ci -fied One, He will your an-swer be.

CHORUS

What will it be? What will it be? Where will you spend your e-ter-ni - ty?

rit.

What will it be, O what will it be? What will your answer be?........

what will it be?

No. 73   I'd Rather Have Jesus

L. G. P.   LUTHER G. PRESLEY

1. Men strive for the wealth of this wide, wicked world, They seek af-ter hon-
2. They seem not to know that their treasures will rust, And thieves of-ten break
3. What prof-it is found in earth's sil-ver and gold? How sad at the close

or and fame; (worldly fame;) So lav-ish-ly sporting their diamonds and pearls,
thru and steal; (often steal;) Con-tent-ed with pleasure, they fol-low their lust,
of life's day, (fleet-ing day,) If for the exchange one must lose his own soul,

They put the dear Sav-ior to shame.
With sor-row their des-ti-ny seal.
From heaven's door be turned a-way.

CHORUS

I'd rath-er live
I'd rath - - - er live in

in that bright ci-ty, Own earth's sil-ver and gold,
heav - - en Than to own all earth's sil-ver and gold,........ I'd

I'd rath-er have Je-sus my Sav-ior Than a
rath - - - er have Je - - sus Than the diamonds of a pal-

I'd Rather Have Jesus

pal - ace to hold; I'd rath-er be just a poor beggar,
aee to hold; .... I'd rath - - - er be a beg - - gar, Live

Live in a shack by the road, Than here to own
in a lit-tle shack by the road, ... Than to own .... all earth's

all of earth's treasures, With no ti-tle to a fu-ture a-bode.
treas - ures, to a fu-ture a-bode ....

No. 74

Revive Us Again

.. MACKAY   J. J. HUSBAND

1. We praise Thee, O God, for the Son of Thy love, For Jesus, who died, and is now gone above.
2. All glory and praise to the Lamb that was slain, Who has borne all our sins and has cleansed ev'ry stain.
3. Revive us again, fill each heart with Thy love, May each soul be rekindled with fire from above.

CHORUS   1   2

Hal - le - lu-jah! Thine the glory, Hal - le - lu - jah! a - men; Re - vive us a-gain.

Don't Forget Jesus

Copyright, 1932, by The Stamps-Baxter Music Co.,
in "Singer's Choice".

Miss Lessie Reddell

R. J. Weaver

1. When you are wea - ry and by sin op-pressed, Trust in the Sav - ior,
2. Tho' you are sad and ev - 'ry-thing seems blue, Don't forget Je - sus
3. If you are drift-ing, tossed a - bout by sin, Don't for - get Je - sus

He can give you rest; He will be with you by night and by day,
for He tho't of you; Pray to the Sav - ior, a new life be - gin,
will help you to win; He is your Sav - ior and on Him re - ly,

CHORUS

Don't for-get Je - sus will hear when you pray.
Je - sus will hear you and save you from sin. Don't for - get Je - sus, the
Some day you'll need Him, the time draweth nigh.

Man of Gal - li - lee, He is so lov-ing, so kind and so true; Don't forget

Je - sus who died on Cal-va-ry, For Je - sus remembered you........
re-membered you.

No. 76 The Garden of Eden in Glory

Copyright, 1932, by The Stamps-Baxter Music Co., in "Singer's Choice"

C. W. Ambrester

J. R. Baxter, Jr.

*Soprano and Alto Duet

1. There's a gar-den of E - den in glo - ry, That our Savior has gone to pre-
2. There's a gar-den of E - den in glo - ry, 'Tis the beau-ti - ful heav-en - ly
3. There's a gar-den of E - den in glo - ry, 'Tis more love-ly than eye here has
4. There's a gar-den of E - den in glo - ry, O dear sinner, don't you want to

pare, Where with all the redeemed in bright mansions, His sweet presence and
goal; What a joy it will be to as - sem - ble With the Sav-ior who
seen, For the walls are all built of pure jas - per And the flow-ers for-
go? Then just give up your sins and trust Je - sus, He will wash your soul

CHORUS

blessings we'll share. There's a gar-den of E - den in glo - - ry,
res-cued my soul.
ev - er are green.
whit-er than snow. glo - ry, in glo - ry,

I am jour-ney-ing on to that place...... Where I'll meet all the saints of the
wonderful place

a - - ges And shall look on my Savior's bright face..........
a-ges, all a - ges His bright face.

*Bass and Tenor may hum to chorus

I Won't Have to Cross Jordan Alone

To my friend V. O. Stamps—C. E. D.

Thomas Ramsey   **Chas. E. Durham**

May be used as a Solo

1. When I come to the riv-er at end-ing of day, When the last winds of
2. Of-ten-times I'm for-sak-en, and wea-ry and sad, When it seems that my
3. Tho' the bil-lows of sorrow and trouble may sweep, Christ the Sav-ior will

sor-row have blown;...... There'll be some-bod-y wait-ing to show me the
friends have all gone;....... There is one tho't that cheers me and makes my heart
care for His own;........ Till the end of the jour-ney, my soul He will

CHORUS

way, I won't have to cross Jor-dan a-lone... I won't have to cross
glad, I won't have to cross Jor-dan a-lone...
keep, I won't have to cross Jor-dan a-lone... I won't have -

Jor-dan a-lone,.......... Je-sus died all my sins to a-tone;
to cross Jor-dan a-lone,

SOLO *ad lib.*   PARTS

When the darkness I see, He'll be waiting for me, I won't have to cross Jordan alone.
Hum.........   Hum..........

Whispering Hope.

G. W. Lyon.   Used by Permission.   J. B. Vaughan.

1. There's light in the val-ley of shad-ows, No long-er the
2. There's hope for the sad and de-spon-dent, Who suf-fer in
3. There's joy for the way-ward and lone-ly, A-far from their
4. There's com-fort and help for the dy-ing, A rod and a

dark-ness I fear; For Je-sus is reign-ing in glo-ry, My
si-lence a-lone; A-mid their be-reave-ments and sor-row, O'er-
own na-tive place; A home and a wel-come are wait-ing, A
staff for the way; A Guide who se-cure-ly will lead them To

CHORUS

strength and my light ev-er near.   Then whis - - - - per-ing
come by the weight of their gloom.
fa-ther with sweet smil-ing face.
realms of an un-cloud-y day.   Whis-per-ing hope, O how

hope,....... O how gen - - - tle thy voice;...... Mak - -
gen-tle thy voice,   Mak-ing my heart in its sor-row re-joice; Whisper-ing

- ing my heart........ In its sor - - - row re - joice......
hope, O how gen-tle thy voice,   Mak-ing my heart in its sorrows re-joice.

No. 79 When He Answered Mother's Prayer

M. P. D.

MARVIN P. DALTON

1. How I loved my saint-ed mother, How I loved her tender care; But the sweet-
2. I can see her in her beaut-y, I can see her snow-white hair; I see God
3. There was joy at home with loved ones, There was joy most ev'ry-where; There was joy

CHORUS

est thing a-bout her, Was that fervant, hum-ble pray'r. Joy
smile down from heaven As He answered mother's pray'r.
a-mong the an-gels When He answerd mother's pray'r. There's a joy that

comes o-ver me stealing, When I think of her
comes o-ver me steal - ing, When I think of mother's sweet pray'r, . .

pray'r, Ne'er lost faith in her Sav-ior, She knew
.... Moth-er nev-er lost faith in her Sav - - - ior, She knew that He al-

In her Sav - - ior,

that He was there; Prayed for home and her
ways was there; .... Mother prayed for her home and her loved

When He Answered Mother's Prayer

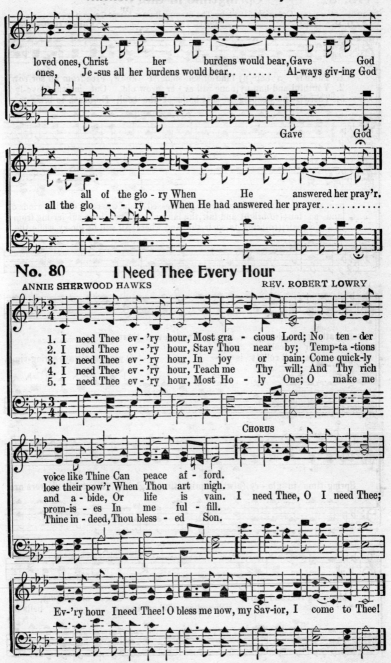

loved ones, Christ her burdens would bear, Gave God
ones, Je-sus all her burdens would bear,...... Al-ways giv-ing God

Gave God

all of the glo - ry When He answered her pray'r.
all the glo - - ry When He had answered her prayer............

No. 80   I Need Thee Every Hour

ANNIE SHERWOOD HAWKS   REV. ROBERT LOWRY

1. I need Thee ev - 'ry hour, Most gra - cious Lord; No ten - der
2. I need Thee ev - 'ry hour, Stay Thou near by; Temp-ta -tions
3. I need Thee ev - 'ry hour, In joy or pain; Come quick-ly
4. I need Thee ev - 'ry hour, Teach me Thy will; And Thy rich
5. I need Thee ev - 'ry hour, Most Ho - ly One; O make me

CHORUS

voice like Thine Can peace af - ford.
lose their pow'r When Thou art nigh.
and a - bide, Or life is vain.   I need Thee, O I need Thee;
prom-is - es In me ful - fill.
Thine in - deed, Thou bless - ed Son.

Ev-'ry hour I need Thee! O bless me now, my Sav-ior, I come to Thee!

Springtime in Glory

L. G. P.

Luther G. Presley

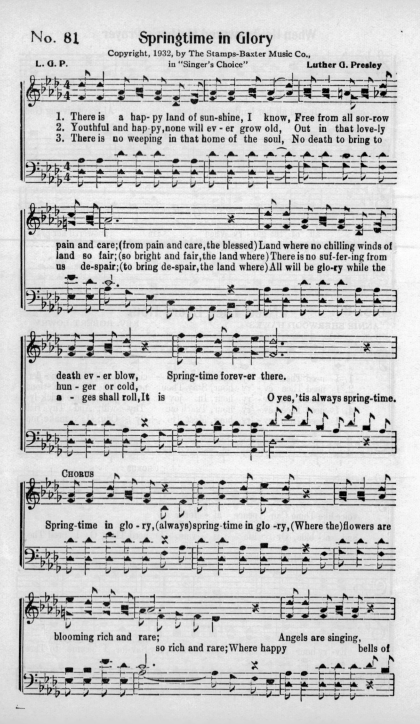

1. There is a hap-py land of sun-shine, I know, Free from all sor-row
2. Youthful and hap-py, none will ev - er grow old, Out in that love-ly
3. There is no weeping in that home of the soul, No death to bring to

pain and care; (from pain and care, the blessed) Land where no chilling winds of
land so fair; (so bright and fair, the land where) There is no suf-fer-ing from
us de-spair; (to bring de-spair, the land where) All will be glo-ry while the

death ev - er blow, Spring-time forev-er there.
hun - ger or cold,
a - ges shall roll, It is O yes, 'tis always spring-time.

CHORUS

Spring-time in glo - ry, (always) spring-time in glo -ry, (Where the) flowers are

blooming rich and rare; Angels are singing,
so rich and rare; Where happy bells of

Springtime in Glory

glo-ry are ring-ing, Spring-time for-ev-er there.

It is 'tis always spring-time

No. 82   Happy in Jesus

J. R. BAXTER, JR. Sug. E. D. C. in "Glory Dawn"   E. D. CULPEPPER

1. Hap-py in Je-sus, tho' burdens I bear, He is sup-ply-ing my needs;
2. Hap-py in Je-sus, I face the dread foe, He will be with me al-way;
3. Hap-py in Je-sus, till life here shall end, Then on that heav-en-ly shore;

He is my comfort, each load He will share, He ev-'ry hungry soul feeds.
He is be-side me wher-ev-er I go, He is my help and my stay.
I shall be-hold Him, my wonderful friend, Live with Him there ev-er-more.

CHORUS

Hap-py in Je-sus, no sin-clouds alarm, Hap-py in Je-sus, I lean on His arm,

Hap-py in Je-sus who shields me from harm; Come and be happy in Him.

A BEAUTIFUL LIFE.

Wm. M. Golden.

1. Each day I'll do a gold-en deed, By help-ing those who are in need; My life on earth is but a span, And so I'll do the best I can. (the best I can.)
2. To be a child of God each day, My light must shine a-long the way; I'll sing His praise while a-ges roll And strive to help some troubled soul. (some troubled soul.)
3. The on-ly life that will en-dure, Is one that's kind and good and pure; And so for God I'll take my stand, Each day I'll lend a help-ing hand. (a help-ing hand.)
4. I'll help some one in time of need, And jour-ney on with rap-id speed; I'll help the sick and poor and weak, And words of kind-ness to them speak. (kind words I'll speak.)
5. While go-ing down life's wea-ry road, I'll try to lift some trav'ler's load; I'll try to turn the night to day, Make flow-ers bloom a-long the way. (the lone-ly way.)

REFRAIN.

Life's ev'ning sun is sinking low, A few more days and I must go To meet the deeds that I have

A Beautiful Life

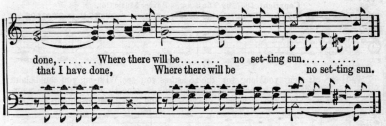

done,........Where there will be........ no set-ting sun..........
that I have done, Where there will be no set-ting sun.

No. 84 My Mother's Song.

Copyright, 1934, in "The Messenger," by Woodie W. Smith Co.

John R. Clements.

F. Degen.
Arr. by W. S. Washington.

1. Mem-'ry paints a pic-ture Ver-y dear to me: In the twi-light
2. Oft - en o'er life's path-way Hangs a cloud of night, But my mother's
3. Oft - en tho' I've wan-dered, Till sin held me bound, I in mother's
4. Something in the mes-sage Al-ways finds my heart, Oft-en as I

seat-ed There at moth-er's knee, Sweet-ly she is hum-ming—Notes al-
Sav - ior Makes the dark-ness bright, As I hear her sing-ing, Joy in
mes-sage Sweet re-lief have found; To my mother's Sav - ior I my
hear it, Will the tear-drops start; Sweet its ben-e-dic-tion—Low my

most di - vine: "My Je - sus, I love Thee, I know Thou art mine."
ev - 'ry line: "My Je - sus, I love Thee, I know Thou art mine."
all re-sign; "My Je - sus, I love Thee, I know Thou art mine."
head I bow: "If ev - er I loved Thee, My Je - sus, 'tis now."

The Best Things of Life are Free

Arr. V. O. S.—L. G. P.   in "Harbor Bells No. 6"   VIRGIL O. STAMPS

1. How oft-en you long for the treasures you see, Wish-ing you could claim
2. Kind words of a friend when your out-look is blue, How they brighten your
3. Trust not in the rich-es of sil-ver and gold, Just re-mem-ber God

them for your own; For-get-ting the best things of this life are free,
hope, like the dawn; The beau-ty of flow-ers that bloom just for you,
sits on His throne; It costs you no mon-ey to en-ter His fold,

CHORUS

Sweetest treasures that the world has ev-er known. You can't
You can't buy the sunshine

buy the sun-shine at midnight, You can't buy the moonlight at dawn,
at mid-night, . . . You can't buy the moonlight at dawn,

You can't buy your youth, when you have grown old, Nor life when your
Nor your life when your heart-beat is

The Best Things of Life are Free

heart-beat is gone; You can't buy the love of a moth-er,
gone;.......... You can't buy the love of a moth-er,......

Nor child - hood a - gain at her knee, Al- tho you may
Nor child-hood a - gain at her knee,..........

hold earth's sil - ver and gold, The best things of life are free..........
best things of this life are free.

No. 86 — On Zion's Hill

Copyright, 1937, by The Stamps-Baxter Music Co., in "Harbor Bells No. 6"

M. H. McK.   M. H. McKEE

1. On Zion's hill a mansion stands For all the pure and blest, We know it was
2. No sun or moon is shining there To light the streets of gold, The Lamb's own
3. To meet you there I mean to live While here on earth I stay, There Christ a

D. S.—The soul's e - ter-nal home; God's voice is

FINE CHORUS   D. S.

was not made with hands, Up there the soul may rest. On Zi - on's blessed hill,
light so wondrous fair The saints with joy behold.
wel-come sweet will give For one e - ter-nal day.   On Zi-on's

soft- ly call-ing still To rest beneath that dome.

My Old Home.

Written especially for my friend and co-worker, Prof. J. E. Thomas.

J. W. E.   Quartet Music Co., owners.   JOE W. EARLS.

1. When I went to the home of my child-hood so dear, Where I once loved so well to
2. I there could not see my mother's sweet face, Nor my father's kind voice could I
3. I went to the spring that was flow-ing so free, And I drank of its wa-ters so
4. Then I went to the place where I once loved to play, But my playmates had ev-'ry one
5. But when I shall reach that heav-en-ly place, The beau-ti-ful cit-y so

roam, How sad and drear, no voice could I hear, There was no one to
hear, How sad did I feel in that lone-ly "old place," Finding no one to
clear, But lone-ly a voice would whis-per to me, "There is no one to
gone, And sad-ly a voice would whis-per and say, "There is no one to
fair, Where I shall be-hold my Re-deem-er's face, There'll be some one to

CHORUS.

welcome me home. No one to welcome me home, ... No one to welcome me home,
welcome me there. welcome me home,
welcome you here." *Chorus for last stanza only.*
welcome you home." Some one to welcome me there, ... In-to that cit-y so fair,
welcome me there. welcome me there,

When I went to the place where I once loved to roam, There was no one to welcome me home.
When I shall be-hold those mansions of gold, There'll be some one to welcome me there.

ROCKING ON THE WAVES

A. B. Sebren

1. I am on the rest-less sea of life, Where no calm-ness comes to
2. Soon my ship will anch-or o-ver there, By the help of Christ the
3. What a glo-rious tho't to feel this way, When the rag-ing tem-pest

still the tide; For 'tis full of dead-ly sin and strife, Rest and
cru-ci-fied; He is help-ing with His un-seen hand, In His
rolls so high; Know-ing He will hear me when I pray,— Sweet-ly

REFRAIN.

peace are on the oth-er side. I am rocking, rocking, rocking on the
arms I'm rocking with the tide.
save me in the by and by. I am

waves, I am rocking on the waves,
rocking, rocking, rocking on the waves,......... I am rocking, rocking, rocking, rocking,

rock-ing, rock-ing, On the o-cean waves;
rock-ing, rock-ing, [Omit............] On the o-cean waves.

Sleep Mother Sleep

Copyright, 1937, by The Stamps-Baxter Music Co.
in "Favorite Radio Songs"

Arr. by E. R.

ERNEST RIPPETOE

1. Home is so lone - ly since moth-er's not there, Dark is her room and va - cant her chair; An - gels have tak - en her out of our care.
2. While she is sleep-ing the sea - sons I know, Cov - er her grave with blos-soms and snow; Snow on the bos - om that shel-tered me so,
3. Her lov-ing eyes were oft dimmed with sad tears, Guid -ing our feet thru long wear - y years; Plan -ning our fu - ture while read-ing God's word,

CHORUS

Still we re - call our dear mother's sweet pray'r. Moth - er sleep, your tri - als are o'er, Sweet be the rest you have need-ed be-fore; We loved
So cold and bleak are the north winds that blow.
Faith - ful and true ad - mo - ni - tions we heard. Sleep, moth-er We all loved

you, but God loved you more, For He called you to that bright hap-py shore.

I Like the Old Time Way

J. R. Baxter, Jr., Suggested by E. W.　　　　　　　　　　　Eugene Wright

1. Man-y to-day think all our fathers were wrong When they believed, Jesus, the
2. Modern in ways, thinking that cul-ture is all, Closing the door when the good
3. Some-one is lost on the bleak mountain of sin, Look-ing for help, hoping the

Mas-ter was strong; Heedless they go careless-ly drift-ing a- long,
Mas-ter shall call; Trusting in self, thinking they never shall fall,
life-crown to win; Man-y will say, "why should I help take him in?" But as for

CHORUS

I like the old time way. I like the old time sing-ing,
me, preaching, praying,

I like the old time way;...... I like the old time
shout-ing, the old time way;

sing-ing, I like the old time way............
preaching, pray-ing, shout-ing, the old time way.

No. 91 Living On the Sunny Side

J. R. BAXTER, JR. M. L. YANDELL

1. Far from the shades of sad-ness I am liv-ing to-day,
2. Prais-es to Christ I'm sing-ing while I jour-ney be-low,
3. This is my true en-deav-or while I trav-el a-long, I'm hap-py,

Look-ing a-bove, trust-ing in love; Soon in a
Safe-ly to
to heav-en, now giv-en; That I may

land of glad-ness I am go-ing to stay, So I'm dai-ly
Je-sus cling-ing when the tempest shall blow,
live for-ev-er in that glad land of song, I'm hap-py, So I'm liv-ing

CHORUS

liv-ing on the sun-ny side. Liv-ing on sun-ny side,
on the sun-ny side. ...... Liv-ing on the sun-ny side, ...

In love I shall a-bide, He is near, naught to
In His love I shall a-bide, He is ev-er near, there is naught to

Living On the Sunny Side

fear, All to Him I con-fide; Storms here beat
fear, All to Him I now con-fide;...... Storms a-round me beat in

now in vain, Safe with Him I'll re-main, Trusting in His love,
vain,........ Safe with Him I shall re-main,........

seek-ing home a-bove, Liv-ing on the beau-ti-ful sun-ny side.
side........

Coda*

Liv-ing on the sun-ny side, Storms of doubt can-not be-tide,
Living on the sun-ny side,...... Storms of doubt cannot be-tide,......

giv-ing, liv-ing On the sun-ny side.
All to Je-sus O the joy of

* After last verse or omitted

The Sunny Side

James Rowe

Claude Goodman

1. If you'd keep away from worry, Whatso-ev-er may be-tide, If you would not
2. You amid the gloom are staying, And each day your strength is tried. Come where sunbeams
3. Thru this world but once you're going Why then in the gloom abide? Live where fragrant

CHORUS

fret or flur-ry, Live up-on the sun-ny side. Just live on the sun-ny
bright are playing, Live up-on the sun-ny side.
flow'rs are growing. Live up-on the sun-ny side. Just live on the sun-ny side of

side, Where the joys of life a - bide, That is where you
life, my brother, Where the joys and pleasures will a - bide, That is where you

ought to be if from wor-ry you'd be free, While the storms are beating,
should be liv - ing if from wor-ry you'd be free, While the storms of life are

and the sea - sons glide, Life is al - ways pleas - ant
beat-ing, and your tri-als you are meeting, Life is al - ways full of cheer and

The Sunny Side

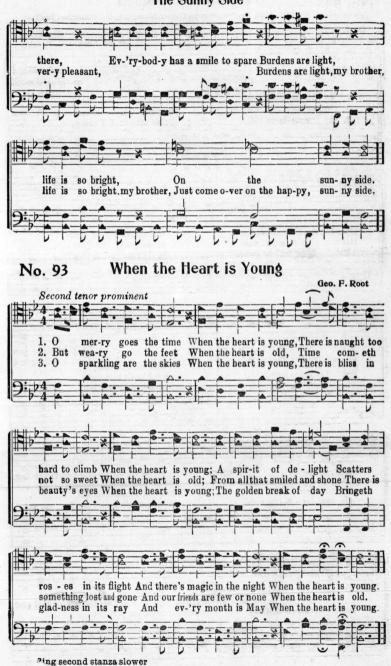

there,   Ev-'ry-bod-y has a smile to spare. Burdens are light,
ver-y pleasant,   Burdens are light, my brother,

life is so bright,   On   the   sun- ny side.
life is so bright, my brother, Just come o-ver on the hap-py, sun- ny side.

No. 93   When the Heart is Young

Geo. F. Root

Second tenor prominent

1. O   mer-ry goes the time When the heart is young, There is naught too
2. But wea-ry go the feet When the heart is old, Time   com- eth
3. O   sparkling are the skies When the heart is young, There is bliss in

hard to climb When the heart is young; A spir-it of de-light Scatters
not so sweet When the heart is old; From all that smiled and shone There is
beauty's eyes When the heart is young; The golden break of day Bringeth

ros - es in its flight And there's magic in the night When the heart is young.
something lost and gone And our friends are few or none When the heart is old.
glad-ness in its ray And   ev'ry month is May When the heart is young.

Sing second stanza slower

No. 94 On the Jericho Road

right, 1933, by The Stamps-Baxter Music Co., in "Boundless Joy".
Donald S. McCrossan, owner

D. S. McC.

Not too fast

Donald S. McCrossan
Arr. by Luther G. Presley

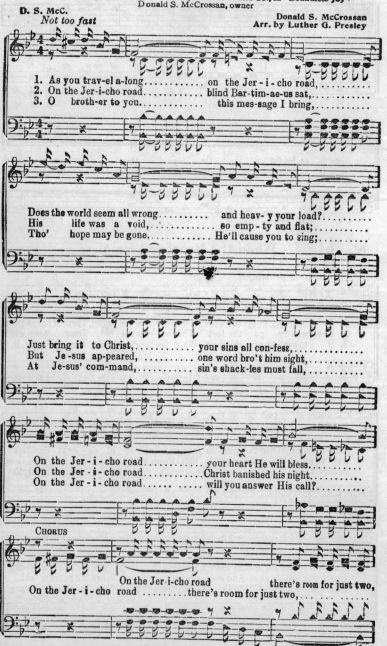

1. As you trav-el a-long............ on the Jer - i - cho road,............
2. On the Jer-i-cho road............ blind Bar-tim-ae-us sat,............
3. O broth-er to you............ this mes-sage I bring,............

Does the world seem all wrong............ and heav- y your load?............
His life was a void,............ so emp - ty and flat;............
Tho' hope may be gone,............ He'll cause you to sing;............

Just bring it to Christ,............ your sins all con-fess,............
But Je-sus ap-peared, ... one word bro't him sight,............
At Je-sus' com-mand,............ sin's shack-les must fall,............

On the Jer - i - cho road............ your heart He will bless............
On the Jer - i - cho road............ Christ banished his night............
On the Jer - i - cho road............ will you answer His call?............

CHORUS

On the Jer-i-cho road there's room for just two,
On the Jer - i - cho road .... there's room for just two,............

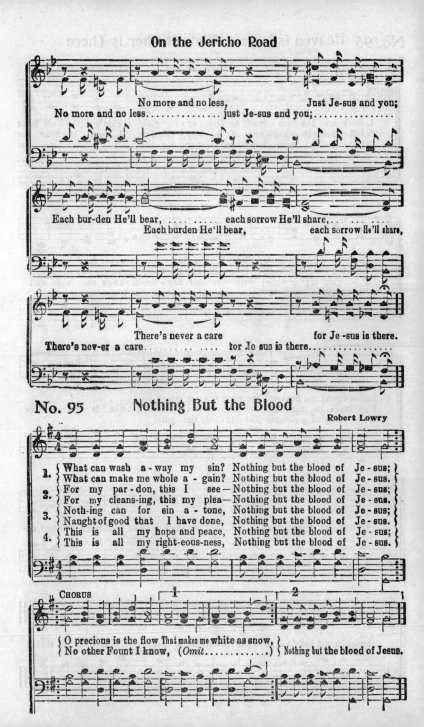

No more and no less, Just Je-sus and you;
No more and no less............ just Je-sus and you;..............

Each bur-den He'll bear,......... each sorrow He'll share,......
Each burden He'll bear, each sorrow He'll share,

There's never a care for Je-sus is there.
There's nev-er a care........ for Je-sus is there..............

No. 95 — Nothing But the Blood

Robert Lowry

1. { What can wash a-way my sin? Nothing but the blood of Je-sus;
   { What can make me whole a-gain? Nothing but the blood of Je-sus.
2. { For my par-don, this I see— Nothing but the blood of Je-sus;
   { For my cleans-ing, this my plea— Nothing but the blood of Je-sus.
3. { Noth-ing can for sin a-tone, Nothing but the blood of Je-sus;
   { Naught of good that I have done, Nothing but the blood of Je-sus.
4. { This is all my hope and peace, Nothing but the blood of Je-sus;
   { This is all my right-eous-ness, Nothing but the blood of Je-sus.

CHORUS

{ O precious is the flow That makes me white as snow,
{ No other Fount I know, (Omit............) } Nothing but the blood of Jesus.

No. 96 Heaven is Nearer Since Mother is There

Copyright, 1937, by The Stamps-Baxter Music Co.,
in "Harbor Bells No. 6"

BLANCHE C. PATTERSON   LUTHER L. LOVETT

1. Dark are the win-dows, no flick-er-ing glow Lights up the old home
2. Oft when the shad-ows of e-ven-tide fall, I seem to hear her
3. O how I miss her sweet voice and her smile, Yet I shall see her

that we used to know; But in the dark-ness a sweet face so fair
voice ten-der-ly call; In words fa-mil-iar, "let's come now to pray'r,"
a-gain aft-er while; With our dear Sav-ior I know she will wait

CHORUS

Smiles down from heav-en for moth-er is there.
I kneel in rev'rence and moth-er is there. Heav-en is near-er since
With a glad wel-come just in-side the gate.

moth-er is there, Heav-en is dear-er since moth-er is there; Earth ties are

brok-en and heav'n is more fair, Heav-en is near-er since moth-er is there.

No 97 Will You Miss Me?

Arr. copyright, 1937, by The Stamps-Baxter Music Co.

REV. GEORGE BEEBE   H. E. McAFEE

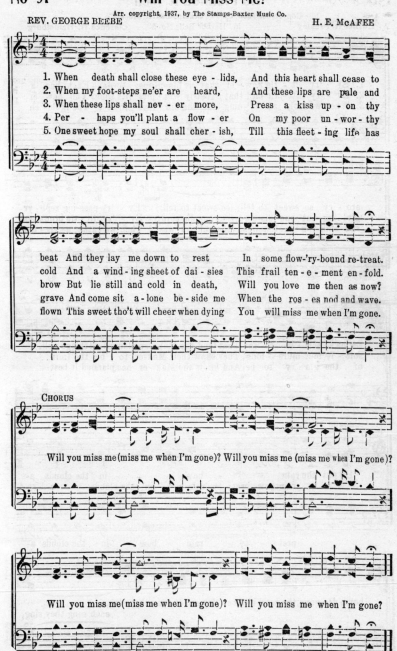

1. When death shall close these eye-lids, And this heart shall cease to beat And they lay me down to rest In some flow'ry-bound re-treat.
2. When my foot-steps ne'er are heard, And these lips are pale and cold And a wind-ing sheet of dai-sies This frail ten-e-ment en-fold.
3. When these lips shall nev-er more, Press a kiss up-on thy brow But lie still and cold in death, Will you love me then as now?
4. Per-haps you'll plant a flow-er On my poor un-wor-thy grave And come sit a-lone be-side me When the ros-es nod and wave.
5. One sweet hope my soul shall cher-ish, Till this fleet-ing life has flown This sweet tho't will cheer when dying You will miss me when I'm gone.

CHORUS

Will you miss me (miss me when I'm gone)? Will you miss me (miss me when I'm gone)?

Will you miss me (miss me when I'm gone)? Will you miss me when I'm gone?

He Planned it Well

Luther G. Presley   Clarence H. Heidelburg

1. Ev - 'ry lit - tle flow - er that is bloom-ing to-day, Each has a
2. Ev - 'ry lit - tle bird that sweet-ly war - bles its song, Tho' nev - er
3. When we look at ev'-ning o'er the hill - tops and see The gold - en

sto - ry so sweet to tell; (so sweet to tell;) Ev - 'ry pass-ing zeph - yr
giv - ing out one dis-cord; (not one dis-cord;) Ev - 'ry lit - tle brook that
sun sink-ing in the west; (the gold-en west;) Then we catch a vis - ion

seems so soft - ly to say That God, the Mak - er, planned all things well....
soft - ly mur-murs a-long, They show their Mak-er to be the Lord....
of the glo - ry to be, And know the Mak - er has planned it best....

CHORUS

He put the rain - - - bow in the clouds a-
rain-bow, pret - ty rain-bow in the clouds

pret - ty rain - bow in the clouds a-

bove, He gave the song birds ev - 'ry sweet song they sing,..........
each song they sing,

He Planned it Well

SWEET HARBOR BELLS

Virgil O. Stamps

1. When the bil-lows rise and roll, Comes this com-fort to my soul,
2. O the hope that they im-part To the wea-ry storm-tossed heart,
3. Till the bless-ed morn shall dawn, Bless-ed bells ring on and on,

Sweet har-bor bells, ring on,............... Precious mes-sage
Ring on,............... ring on,............... Till our Pi-lot's
sweet har-bor bells; Tell-ing us that

from the strand Of the bless-ed glo-ry-land; Ring on, ring
home is near, Bid-ding us be of good cheer;
face we see, Ev-er more our comfort be; sweet har-bor bells,

CHORUS

on............... Oh, hear them ring, Giving com-fort ev-er
sweet har-bor bells. Ring on,...............

cres.

more; What cheer they bring from the hap-py gold-en shore.
Ring on,...............

Virgil O. Stamps, owner,

SWEET HARBOR BELLS

No. 100 When Jesus Comes.

J. W. G.

Copyright, 1923, by J. W. Gaines.

J. W. Gaines.

1. When Je - sus comes a - gain to gath - er His own, And to the true, a
2. I want to tell to all the sto - ry of love, That they may know His
3. He's com - ing back a - gain, His jew - els to claim, They shall re - ceive e -
4. I do not know the day my Sav - iour will come, But I must be pre -

crown is giv'n, I want to hear Him say, "My serv - ant, well done,
par - don free; And there be - fore His throne in glo - ry a - bove,
ter - nal rest; 'Tis sweet to know that all who come in His name,
pared to go; If I am read - y He will call me His own,

FINE. CHORUS.

Thy soul shall know the joys of heav'n".
Re - ceive a crown of vic - to - ry.
Shall there be num - bered with the blest.
And that's e - nough for me to know.

I want to know that
I want to know that He

D. S.—And ev - er there with Him a - bide.

He will welcome me there, I do not want to be de -
will welcome me there, I do not want to be de -

D. S.

nied; I want to meet Him in that cit - y so fair,
nied; I want to meet Him in that cit - y so fair,

Turn Away

B. E.   Rev. B. B. Edmiaston

1. Dear comrade, you're fac-ing the right and the wrong, The tempter to sin
2. Your du-ty lies out on the road that is straight, Some crosses each pil-
3. This life is so short and there's so much to do If vic-to-ry's crown
4. The temp-ter is striv-ing to call some a-way From mer-cy and par-

would al-lure, (would allure,) He'd blind you and weaken the life that is strong,
grim must bear;.......... The throng would delay you un-til 'tis too late,
(pa-tient-ly bear;)
we would win, (we would win,) Each day we must bravely to du-ty be true,
don and love, O fol-low him not for he lead-eth a-stray,
won-der-ful love,

Chorus

Turn a-way and thus keep your soul pure. O don't be-
Turn a-way and seek Je-sus in prayer.
Turn a-way from temp-ta-tion and sin.
Turn a-way and seek heav-en a-bove. O heed not the temp-ter, don't

gin,.......... Lest wrong should win;.......... Turn a-
ev-er be-gin, Lest o-ver your spir-it the e-vil should win;

way, turn a-way, turn a-way, turn a-way, Turn away from temptation and sin.

For Me

B. B. Edmiaston

Emmett S. Dean

1. For me (the Lord prayed,) He prayed, (for re-lief,) For me, for
2. For me (He was slain,) He died (on the cross,)
3. For me (dead in sin,) He 'rose (from the grave,) for me,

me;.......... A-lone, (His heart broke,) a-lone, (He bore grief,)
In shame (be-tween thieves,) in shame, (and deep loss,)
for me; With pow'r (sub-dued death,) with pow'r, (me to save,)

CHORUS *Faster*

For me.......... for me.......... Glo-ry to God! He's
for me. for me.

com-ing a-gain, Com-ing to earth for me;
He's com-ing for me;

King of all kings, my Sav-iour will reign, In all e-ter-ni-ty.

No. 103   Where We'll Never Grow Old

To my father and mother.—J. C. M.

Copyright, 1930, by Jas. C. Moore

JAS. C. MOORE

1. I have heard of a land on the far a-way strand, 'Tis a beau-ti-ful home of the soul; Built by Je-sus on high, there we nev-er shall die,

2. In that beau-ti-ful home where we'll nev-er-more roam, We shall be in the sweet by and by; Hap-py praise to the King thru e-ter-ni-ty sing,

3. When our work here is done and our life-crown is won, And our troubles and tri-als are o'er; All our sor-row will end, and our voic-es will blend,

'Tis a land where we nev-er grow old.
'Tis a land where we nev-er shall die.
With the loved ones who've gone on be-fore.

Chorus

Nev-er grow old, where we'll nev-er grow old, In a land where we'll nev-er grow old; Nev-er grow old, where we'll nev-er grow old, In a land where we'll never grow old.

No. 104 In The Sunshine Of His Blessed Love

C. D.

Cleavant Derricks

1. I am trusting in my bless-ed Sav-ior Who is all the world to me,
2. I am walk-ing dai - ly with my Sav-ior On the up-ward pil-grim way,
3. Yes, I dear - ly love my bless-ed Sav-ior For He paid the price for me,

With His arms of faith He will sur-round me, Ev - er faith-ful I shall
That is why the jour - ney is so peace-ful, Lead-ing to e - ter - nal
More than all He clears the way be - fore me, That the sun-shine I may

be;...... Since my soul is rest-ing in His keep-ing, I am fac - ing
day;.... I can feel His bless - ed pres-ence near me As I wend my
see;...... Yes, He al-ways hears my earn - est plead-ing As I look to

home a - bove, I'm con-tent to rest on His gen - tle breast, In the sun-shine
way a - bove, I shall reach my goal, home-land of the soul, In the sun-shine
Him a - bove, Safe with Him I'll be and His face I'll see In the sun-shine

CHORUS

of His bless-ed love.   Trust - ing   Him
                      I am trust-ing in my Sav - ior ev - 'ry

In The Sunshine Of His Blessed Love

ev - 'ry day   As   I   go   on my way,
day   As I jour - ney on my up - ward pil - grim way,

All   to   me,   faith - ful   be,   March-ing
He   is all the world to me, ev - er faith-ful I shall be, Marching to   my

home a - bove;......   Speaks   to   me   as   I go,
O He speaks to me so sweet-ly as I go,

He   will   guide   here be - low, I'm con-tent to
And will guide me thru this wild - er - ness be - low,

rest on His gen - tle breast In the sun-shine of His bless-ed love......

MUSIC IN MY SOUL.

Rev. Johnson Oatman, Jr.

L. B. Harris.

1. There is mu-sic in my soul, While from my lips hal-le-lu-jahs roll, Since
2. There is mu-sic in my soul, Since by His blood I have been made whole, And
3. There is mu-sic in my soul, O Saviour, help me Thy praise ex-tol, Un-

Je-sus loosed my bonds and gave me sweet re-lease; Tossed no more up-on life's wave, Since
now I try to live like Je-sus ev-'ry day; So that all the world may see, The
til it reach-es to the arches of the sky; So that all the world may hear, The

Je-sus all my sins for-gave, For now He reigns within my heart the Prince of Peace.
blessed Christ revealed thru me, And that I may a bless-ing be up-on life's way.
name to us of all most dear, As we re-ech-o "Glo-ry be to God on high."

CHORUS.

There is mu-sic in my soul, Let the glad hal-le-
There is mu-sic in my soul, Let the hal-le-
There is mu-sic, mu-sic in my soul, Let the glad hal-le-
There is mu-sic ring-ing in my

lu-jahs roll, All a-long my pil-grim way my
lu-jahs roll, All a-long my pil-grim way my
lu-jahs roll, All a-long my pil-grim way my song of
soul, All a-long my pil-grim way my

R. N. Grisham

song of praise I sing;   My Sav - - - iour   set   me

song of praise I sing;   For my Seviour set me free, And He is so
praise I glad-ly sing;   My Sav-iour   set my   spir-it

song of praise I joy-ful-ly sing: For my Saviour set me free, And He is so

free,   Now all the way, ev-'ry day, I will make His praises ring,
good to me,   glad-ly ring.

No. 106   LET THE LOWER LIGHTS BE BURNING.

P. P. B.   Matt. 5: 16.   P. P. Bliss.

1. Bright-ly beams our Fa-ther's mer - cy, From His light-house ev - er - more,
2. Dark the night of sin has set - tled, Loud the an - gry bil - lows roar;
3. Trim your feeb - le lamp, my broth - er; Some poor sail - or tem - pest tossed,

FINE.

But to us He gives the keep - ing   Of the lights a - long the shore.
Eag - er eyes are watch-ing, long-ing,   For the lights a - long the shore.
Try - ing now to make the har - bor, In the dark-ness may be lost.

D. S.—Some poor faint-ing, struggling sea-man, You may res - cue, you may save.

CHORUS.   D. S.

Let the low - er lights be burn-ing! Send a gleam a - cross the wave!

I Want My Life to Testify

W. O. C.

O. H. Cundiff, owner

W. Oliver Cooper

1. I want my life to show the world that I am do-ing right, I
2. I want my eyes to see the glo-ry of my Sav-ior's love, I
3. I want my hands to lift the fall-en from the mire of sin, I

want my voice to sing God's praise from morning un-til night; I want my
want my ears to lis-ten to His or-ders from a-bove; I want my
want to lead them back to right and help them vic-t'ry win; I want to

feet to keep me walk-ing al-ways in the light; I want my life..........
ev-'ry step to be an-oth-er homeward move;
live so I may have full con-fi-dence of men;   I want my life

REFRAIN

to tes-ti-fy............   I want to ev-er love and serve my blessed
        to tes-ti-fy.   I want to   serve   my
        I want to know He always hears me, always
        I want   to   know   He

Master ev-'ry day, I want to always walk within my God's appointed way;
hears me when I pray, I want   to   walk   in God's appointed way;

I Want My Life to Testify

want my life to tell, O yes, I
want my life to tes - ti - fy.....................
want my life to tell, I want my life to tes - ti - fy.

No. 108   Love

Copyright, 1934, by The Stamps-Baxter Music Co.,
in "Harbor Bells No. 3"   Mrs. Lillian McMahan

1. Love of the Father so wondrous and true, Love coming down for me and for you;
2. Love that sent Jesus to die on the tree, Love that would save a sinner like me;
3. Love that will help us each burden to bear, Love that delights our troubles to share;

Hum

Love that is boundless, 'tis old, yet 'tis new, Love, God's wonderful love.
Love that could pardon, from bonds set us free, Love, God's wonderful love.
Love that will dai - ly re - lieve us of care, Love, God's wonderful love.

CHORUS

Love, love, full and free, Love, love for sin-ners like me;
Love of the Father, so full and so free, Love coming down for a sinner like me;

Love, boundless love, from the Father a-bove, Love, God's wonderful love.

O Happy Day.

Philip Doddridge.   L. B. Harris, owner.   By per.   Arr. by L. B. Harris.

1. O hap-py day............ that fixed my choice............
2. O hap-py bond............ that seals my vows............
3. 'Tis done, the great .... trans-ac-tion's done!............

On Thee, my Sav — — iour and my God! (the liv-ing God!)
To Him who mer — — its all my love! (yes, all my love!)
I am my Lord's............ and He is mine; (He's tru-ly mine;)

Well may this glow — — ing heart re - joice,............
Let cheer-ful an — — thems fill His house,............
He drew me, and............ I fol-lowed on,............

And tell its rap — — tures all a - broad. (a - broad.)
While to that sa — — cred shrine I move. (I move.)
Charmed to con - fess...... the voice di - vine. (di - vine.)

CHORUS.

He taught me how............ to watch and pray,............

He taught me how   to   pray, to watch and pray,
He taught me how   to   pray, to watch and pray.

He taught   me   how   to   pray, to watch and pray,

O Happy Day.

And live re-joic - - ing ev-'ry day;......... .. ..

And live re-joic-ing ev-'ry day;.............

And live re-joic-ing ev-'ry pass-ing day;

And live re - joic - ing ev-'ry pass-ing day;

O hap-py day,.............. O hap-py day, ...

O hap-py day, O hap-py day,......... ....

O hal - le - lu - jah,........... O hap-py day,

Hap-py day, blest hap-py day,

When Je-sus washed............ my sins a - way...............

When Je-sus washed my sins a - way, my sins a-way.

No. 110   Cross And Crown.

Thos. Shepherd.

Geo. N. Allen.

1. Must Je - sus bear the cross a - lone, And all the world go free?
2. The con - se - cra - ted cross I'll bear, Till death shall set me free;
3. O pre-cious cross! O glo-rious crown! O res - ur - rec-tion day!

No there's a cross for ev -'ry one, And there's a cross for me.
And then go home my crown to win, For there's a crown for me.
Ye an - gels from the stars come down, And bear my soul a - way.

Sing His Praise

J. R. B., Jr.

J. R. Baxter, Jr., owner.

J. R. Baxter, Jr.

1. Sing the praise of Je-sus as you go a-long, Sing a-bout His goodness,
2. Sing a-bout the Man who came from Gal-i-lee, Sing a-bout the blood He
3. Sing of full sal-va-tion purchased on the tree, Sing of sav-ing grace that

sing it loud and strong; Sing a-bout His mer-cy, sing a-bout His grace,
shed for you and me; Sing a-bout His voice that winds and waves o-bey,
sets the cap-tive free; Sing of all His heal-ing of the halt, the lame,

Sing a-bout His death to save a fall-en race: Give Him ad-o-ra-tion,
Sing a-bout His love that rules the world to-day: Give Him all the glo-ry
Sing a-bout His teaching, ev-'rywhere the same: Give Him your best service

homage, praise and love, Crown Him King of earth and King of heav'n above; Un-to
ev-'ry-where you go, Help to spread His kingdom, precious seed to sow; Show your
while you tarry here, With Him as your Captain, foes you need not fear; Sing a-

Him all honor and all praise belong, Sing the song of triumph, sing the victor's song.
love for Je-sus in your dai-ly life. Help to sing His gospel here amid the strife.
bout His bursting all the bonds of sin, Sing about His coming back to earth again.

Sing His Praise

Bass Solo

Sing a-loud His prais-es, tell a-broad His fame, Mag-ni-fy His hon-or, glo-ri-fy His name; Shout it from the hill-tops, make it swell and ring, Join in ex-ul-ta-tion, He is Lord and King!

CHORUS

Crown Him Lord and King to-day,
Crown the blessed Sav-ior, Lord and King to-day,

Praise Him all a-long the way; Sing till
Praise His name to-geth-er all a-long the way; Sing a-loud His praise till

earth its trib-ute brings, To the feet of Je-sus, He is King of kings.

No. 112
'TWILL NOT BE LONG

V. O. S.

Virgil O. Stamps

DUET Slow

1. Some day the cares of life will rise, Some day we'll be in
2. The toils of life will soon be past, Our bur-dens at His
3. Our loved ones in that home we'll see, At rest with them we'll

Par - a - dise; Then our dear Lord will right each wrong,
feet we'll cast; Then right shall take the place of wrong,
ev - er be; In dreams some-times I hear their song,

CHORUS *All Parts*
Faster

Oh! praise His name, 'twill not be long. 'Twill not be long, 'twill not be
Oh! hap-py tho't, 'twill not be long.
We soon shall meet, 'twill not be long. 'Twill not be long, 'twill

long 'Till right shall take the place of wrong; Look up and
not be long, 'Till right shall take the place of wrong; Look

smile, and sing a song, Oh, praise the Lord, 'twill not be long.
up and smile, and sing a song, Oh, praise the Lord, 'twill not be long.

Let Me Live Close to Thee

J. R. Baxter, Jr. Copyright, 1927, by V. O. Stamps Virgil O. Stamps

1. In Thy field I would wield sick-les brave and true, In the fight for the right
2. Not the crown nor renown that the world might see, I would work, never shirk,
3. Help me bear and to share some poor pilgrim's load, Be my friend to the end

I would dare and do, Spend my days in Thy praise all the journey thru, Let me
blessed Lord, for Thee, But to know where I go that my soul is free, Let me
of the toilsome road, I would sing to my King in the soul's a-bode, Let me

CHORUS

live close to Thee each day. Let me live.... close to Thee, Take my
Let me live   close to Thee,

hand, dear Lord, and guide me all along the rug-ged way; O let me live....
Guide   me   all   a - long   the   way;   Let me live

Let   me   walk   close to Thee each day.
close to Thee, ... Let me walk and talk with Thee, dear Lord, each day.
close to Thee,

No. 114   Wondrous Light of Heaven

Dedicated to The Jay Quartet of Florida

C. T.   Arr. by Cawthon Thompson

1. There's a wondrous light in heav-en, the light of Christ di-vine, Send-ing
2. Christ, the wondrous light of heaven, needs help-ers ev-'ry-where Who will
3. We must dai-ly work for Je-sus while thru this world we go If we

down a ray of love for ev-'ry soul; But in death's dark valley dy-ing
gladly teach and sing and preach and pray, His re-ward for those who help Him
hope to win a home in heav'n a-bove, We must seek the way-ward sin-ner

f.   FINE.

are friends of yours and mine, Who have failed to see the light or gain the goal.
is joy be-yond com-pare, O my broth-er, let us spread His light to-day.
and res-cue Him from woe, Help-ing Him to see the light of Je-sus' love.

D. S.—*Till at last in heav'n we reach the shining goal.*

CHORUS

Bless-ed Father, Savior, Je-sus, Help us see the light; May we follow where it

leads us, To that home so bright; Blessed Father, Savior, Jesus, Help us change some

wand'ring soul;　　　　　Call us where Thy service needs us,
some precious, wand'ring soul and

No. 115　　We Shall Rise

Copyright, 1935, by The Stamps-Baxter Music Co.,
in "Harbor Bells No. 4"

C. B.　　　　　　　　　　　　　　　　　Carlos Barrentine

1. When the Lord of all both the great and small Shall declare that time's no more
2. When the dead shall rise to the vaulted skies, We that live shall see the sight;
3. If we will be-lieve free-ly we'll re-ceive Life a-bund-ant glad and free,

Then the saints shall rise, meet Him in the skies, Heaven's regions to ex-plore.
Quick-ly we shall change to the glo-ry range, O-ver there will be no night.
When He comes again peace and joy shall reign, With the Sav-ior we shall be.

CHORUS

we shall rise,........ we shall rise In the res-ur-rec-tion
We shall rise,..........we shall rise,...........Glo-ry, glo-ry hal-le-

morn-ing we shall rise;　　　　　　　yes, we shall rise.
(Omit..................) lu-jah, we shall rise.

Singing While Ages Roll

O. A. P.

O. A. Parris

1. Some day, glad day, on heav-en's gold-en shore, (bright shore,) We'll
2. What joy to be with all that hap-py band, (glad band,) From
3. In that sweet clime, the home-land of the soul, (the soul,) Our

sing God's praise With those gone on be - fore, No sin or
sin be free There in that lovely land; We'll sing and
songs will ring While end-less a-ges roll; All doubts and

No sin or pain, no

pain, will reach us o - ver there, (o'er there,) Where all is
shout His prais-es o'er and o'er, (and o'er,) As years go
fears will be so far a - way, (a-way,) A thou - sand

sin or pain, Where all is love, where

CHORUS

love and joy be-yond com-pare. (compare.) We'll sing God's praise thru
by we'll learn to love Him more. (and more.)
years will seem as but a day. (short day.)

all is love,

end-less days, On that bright golden shore, Glad praise we shall out-
On that bright gold-en shore, Glad praise we

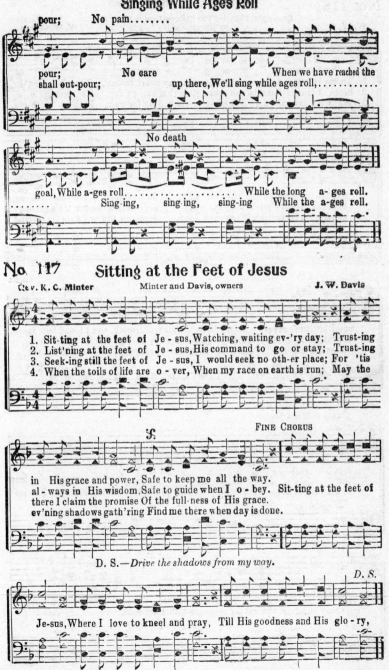

pour; No pain........ No care When we have reached the

pour; shall out-pour; up there, We'll sing while ages roll,............

No death

goal, While a-ges roll.................... While the long a-ges roll.

.... Sing-ing, sing-ing, sing-ing While the a-ges roll.

No. 117 Sitting at the Feet of Jesus

Rev. K. C. Minter   Minter and Davis, owners   J. W. Davis

1. Sit-ting at the feet of Je-sus, Watching, waiting ev-'ry day; Trust-ing
2. List'ning at the feet of Je-sus, His command to go or stay; Trust-ing
3. Seek-ing still the feet of Je-sus, I would seek no oth-er place; For 'tis
4. When the toils of life are o-ver, When my race on earth is run; May the

FINE   CHORUS

in His grace and power, Safe to keep me all the way.
al-ways in His wisdom, Safe to guide when I o-bey. Sit-ting at the feet of
there I claim the promise Of the full-ness of His grace.
ev'ning shadows gath'ring Find me there when day is done.

D. S.—*Drive the shadows from my way.*

D. S.

Je-sus, Where I love to kneel and pray, Till His goodness and His glo-ry,

Jesus Is Mine

W. W. C.

W. W. Combs

DUET *Slowly*

1. There is joy and peace and gladness in my heart to-day, There's a song to
2. Since I 'rose His name con-fessing, on that hap-py day, He has giv'n a-
3. What He did for me and oth-ers, He will do for you, Fathers, moth-ers,

ban-ish sad-ness on the heart-ward way; Je-sus gave to me this bless-ing,
bundant blessing all a-long the way; Rich-er joy to me He's giv-ing
sisters, brothers, He will save you, too; Then you, too, will praise Him singing

Parts   *rit.*

as I knelt in prayer, Then I 'rose His name confessing, when I found Him there.
as the hills I climb, Since for Him I'm daily liv-ing, He is ev-er mine.
just as oth-ers do, Keep the tidings ev-er ring-ing, Je-sus died for you.

CHORUS *Much faster*

Now   I   am   free,   Since
Now I trav-el home-ward singing, and my soul is free from sin, Since my Sav-ior
                                                      ev-er

then   there's   peace with-in; All my burdens roll'd a-way,
heard my pleading, there is joy and peace within my soul,........ As I go

Jesus Is Mine

on that hap-py, hap-py day,   Je-sus then gave me a   song,
on............. He giv-eth me...................... to praise Him;

So I live in con-tem-pla-tion, Since I knelt at His dear feet,
So,   now I live   feel-ing no

There is no more con-dem - na-tion, I have hap-pi-ness complete,
dread,   no   con - dem - na - tion,   go-ing a-

Now I sing each day,   on the glo-ry way   And I'm
long,   sing-ing a song,   Praising His name,.....

glad that I can tru-ly say that He is ev-er mine..............
        say   Je - sus is mine, for-ev-er mine.
    for   Je - - - sus

Jesus Paid It All

ARRANGEMENT COPYRIGHT, 1925, BY J. W. GAINES

Mrs. M. M. Hall

Jno. T. Grape
Arr. by J. W. Gaines

1. I hear the Savior say, hear the Savior say, "Thy strength... in-deed is
1. I hear .... the Sav-ior say, "Thy strength indeed is small,
2. Lord, now indeed I find, now indeed I find, Thy pow'r, ... and Thine a-
2. Lord, now .... in-deed I find, Thy pow'r, and Thine alone,
3. For nothing good have I, nothing good have I, Whereby...... Thy grace to
3. For noth - - - ing good have I, Whereby Thy grace to claim—
4. And when, before the throne, when before the throne, I stand .... in Him com-
4. And when, ... be-fore the throne, I stand in Him complete,

small, Child of weakness, watch and pray, ev-er watch and pray,
strength indeed is small, Child of weak - - ness, watch and pray,
lone, Can change the leper's spots, change the lep-er's spots,
pow'r, and Thine a-lone, Can change .... the lep-er's spots,
claim— I'll wash my garments white, wash my garments white,
sav - ing grace to claim—I'll wash .... my garments white,
plete, "Je-sus died my soul to save," "died my soul to save,"
stand in Him complete, "Je-sus died .... my soul to save,"

CHORUS.

Find in Me Thine all in all." (thine all in all.") Je-sus paid it all,
And.... melt the heart of stone. (the heart of stone.)
In the blood of Calv'ry's Lamb. (of Calv'ry's Lamb.)
My.... lips shall still re-peat. (shall still re-peat.) Je - - sus paid it

Je-sus paid it all, All to Him I owe, I owe; ....
all, All to Him I owe; ....

He opened wide the cleansing fountain,

Jesus Paid It All

Sin had left a stain, a crim-son stain, He washed it white as snow.
Sin had left yes white as snow.

No. 120   Is It Well With Your Soul?

V. O. Stamps, owner

VIRGIL O. STAMPS

1. 'Mid the toil and strife of this bu-sy life,
2. Have you lost your sin, are you pure with-in?
3. Do you praise the love of the One a-bove? Is it well

Is it well

with your soul? Are you liv-ing right, should you die to-night?
Are you at the side of the cru-ci-fied?
Will the crown be won and the Lord's "well done?"

with your soul?

D.S.- Are you liv-ing right should you die to-night?

FINE.   CHORUS

Is it well with your soul?   Is it well

Is it well   Is it well

Is it well___ with your soul?

D. S.

with your soul,   Are you free, glad and whole?

with your soul,   Are you free,   glad and whole?

No. 121 I Just Can't Keep From Crying Sometime

Dedicated to Mrs. Eugenia Gay—C. D.

C. D.

Cleavant Derricks

1. Sometimes I get wea-ry all a-long my pil-grim way, And sor-rows
2. Sometimes I am troubl-ed, I am troubled in my soul, And heav-y
3. Well, I have a moth-er ov-er on the oth-er side, I know that

seem to press me ev-'ry time I kneel to pray; Troubles seem to
burd-ens press me when I try to reach the goal; Friends and kind-red
I shall meet her when I cross the great di-vide; Well, I feel her

gath-er round me ev-'ry mo-ment of the day, And I just can't
seem to doubt me and it makes my heart grow cold, And
pres-ence near me, and I know the storm I'll ride, But

CHORUS

keep from cry-ing some-time........ Well I just can't keep from
some-time.

cry-ing all a-long my pil-grim way, When my heart is bowed with

I Just Can't Keep From Crying Sometime

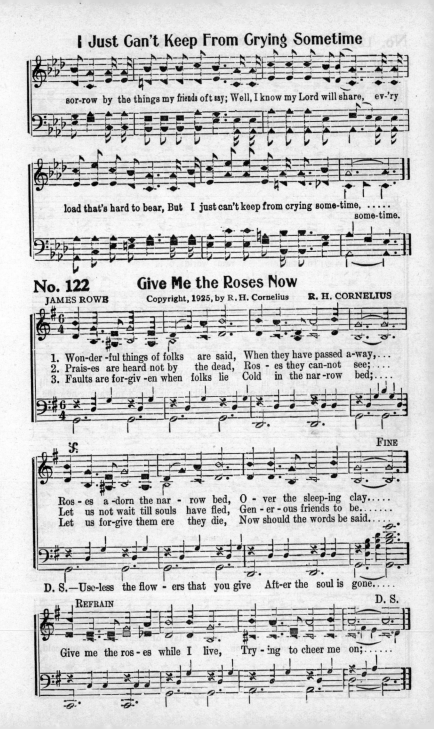

sor-row by the things my friends oft say; Well, I know my Lord will share, ev'ry

load that's hard to bear, But I just can't keep from crying some-time, ...
some-time.

No. 122 Give Me the Roses Now

JAMES ROWE   Copyright, 1925, by R. H. Cornelius   R. H. CORNELIUS

1. Won-der-ful things of folks are said, When they have passed a-way,....
2. Prais-es are heard not by the dead, Ros-es they can-not see;....
3. Faults are for-giv-en when folks lie Cold in the nar-row bed;....

FINE

Ros-es a-dorn the nar-row bed, O-ver the sleep-ing clay.....
Let us not wait till souls have fled, Gen-er-ous friends to be.......
Let us for-give them ere they die, Now should the words be said.....

D. S.—Use-less the flow-ers that you give Aft-er the soul is gone.....

REFRAIN   D. S.

Give me the ros-es while I live, Try-ing to cheer me on;......

The Sunset Pass

L. G. P. Luther G. Presley

1. I've just a lit-tle lon-ger on the road to trav-el here be-
2. I'm hit-ting up the trail that Je-sus made a-cross the hills of
3. So man-y of my friends have gone before, they're just a-cross the

low, (be-low,) In this vain world there is nothing that can
time, (of time,) In this........ vain world......
range (the range) In this........ vain world......

last; ..... I soon shall lay a-side this heav-y load and fold my tent to
I trav-el in a land where flowers fade, soon ev'ning bells will
can last; And trav'ling days for me will soon be o'er, I'm waiting now the

go, (to go,) For just a-head is the sun-set pass.......
chime, (will chime,) For just ..... a-head ..... sun-set pass.
change, (the change,) sun-set pass.

CHORUS

I'm trudg - ing on ..... thru the days of heat and cold,. .
Trudging on, trudg-ing on and cold,

The Sunset Pass

To that land, hap - py land where none ev - er grow old;
To that.... fair land.... where they say none ev-er grow old;.......

How sweet.......'twill be..... there to join my childhood class,....
Sweet it will be, sweet it will be childhood class,

Wait - ing me, wait - ing me at the sun - set pass........
Now wait - - ing me..... sun - set pass.

No. 124   Nearer, My God, to Thee

Sarah F. Adams   Lowell Mason

1. Near- er, my God, to Thee, Near- er to Thee; E'en tho' it be a cross
2. Tho' like a wan-der-er, The sun gone down, Dark-ness be o - ver me,
3. There let the way ap-pear Steps un-to heav'n, All that Thou sendest me,

D. S.—*Near-er, my God, to Thee,*

FINE   D. S.

That rais- eth me; Still all my song shall be, Near-er, my God, to Thee,
My   rest a stone; Yet in my dreams I'd be Near-er, my God, to Thee,
In   mer-cy giv'n; An - gels to beck-on me Near-er, my God, to Thee,

Near - er to Thee!

No. 125 I DREAMED I SEARCHED HEAVEN FOR YOU.

Mary Ethel Wiess.

James D. Vaughan.

Very slow, with expression.

1. I dreamed I had gone to that cit - y, That cit - y where
2. I looked on both sides of the riv - er That flows thro' the
3. I asked of ten thou-sand sweet an - gels, Have you seen this be-

nev - er comes night, And I saw the bright an-gels in glo - ry, I
cit - y of God; I searched thro' bright mansions ce - les - tial, And
lov'd one? pray tell, Have you met in the bright courts of heav - en That

saw the fair man-sions of light. I gazed for long, long years of rap - ture,
streets of gold pavement I trod; The fa - ces of saints by the mil - lion
one whom on earth we loved well? They shook their heads sadly and told me

On the face of my Sav - iour so true, And I sang with the
I scanned in my yearn - ing to see That face I had
That they had not seen you, and then I knew that some-

ser - a - phim ho - ly,— Then I dreamed I searched heav-en for you.
cherished so fond - ly,— The face that had grown dear to me.
where in the dark-ness You wan-dered, lost, lost in sin.

CHORUS.

I dreamed I searched heav-en for you, ... Searched vain-ly thru
for you,

heav-en for you;......... Friend, won't you pre-pare to
for you;

meet me up there? Lest we should search heav-en for you.

No. 126   THE SWEETEST NAME!

Frederick Whitfield.   Lowell Mason.

1. There is a name I love to hear, I love to speak its worth;
2. It tells me of a Sav-iour's love, Who died to set me free;
3. Je - sus! the name I love so well, The name I love to hear!
4. This name shall shed its fra-grance still A - long this thorn - y road;

It sounds like mu - sic in mine ear—The sweet-est name on earth.
It tells me of His pre - cious blood, The sin - ner's per - fect plea.
No saint on earth its worth can tell, No heart con-ceive how dear.
Shall sweetly smoothe the rug - ged hill That leads me up to God.

Look How This World Has Made.

Arr. by J. B. V.　　　By per. of J. B. Vaughan, owner.　　　Arr. by J. B. VAUGHAN.

1. We see our friends are weeping, with their bad-ges on their door, We
2. Our friends are pass-ing o-ver to some far dis-tant shore, We
3. Dear sin-ner, oh, get read-y, you must meet your God on high, For

see their home in moaning, for their lov'd ones come no more; You can
seek them and we call them, but they an-swer us no more. The
death is all a-round you and it will not pass you by, Death

say just what you please, death rides on ev-'ry breeze, Look how this world has
throbbing hearts to-day, to-mor-row pass a-way, Look how this world has
knocks at ev-'ry door, no mat-ter where you go, Look how this world has

CHORUS.

made a change. Just look how this world has made a change, Just
made a change,

look how this world has made a change; You can see ev-'ry day,
made a change;

Look How This World Has Made.

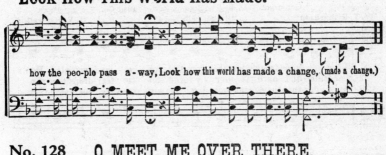

how the peo-ple pass a-way, Look how this world has made a change, (made a change.)

No. 128   O MEET ME OVER THERE.

MOLLIE FERGUSON.   J. H. GAINES.

1. A hap-py home is wait-ing me, A home that's bright and fair;
2. I'll see my Sav-iour as He is, And in His glo-ry share;
3. Sweet songs of praise I'll ev-er sing, And robes of white I'll wear,

A home where I, my Lord, shall see,—O meet me o-ver there!
En-joy His love for ev-er-more—O meet me o-ver there!
A-round the throne of Christ, my King,—O meet me o-ver there!

REFRAIN.

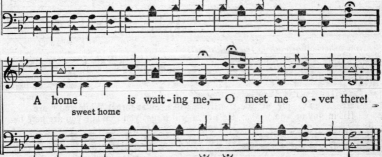

A home is wait-ing me, I, soon, its joys shall share;
sweet home   I, soon

A home is wait-ing me,— O meet me o-ver there!
sweet home

By permission,

No. 129 Jesus Remembers When Others Forget

W. T. Richardson

H. V. Bagwell

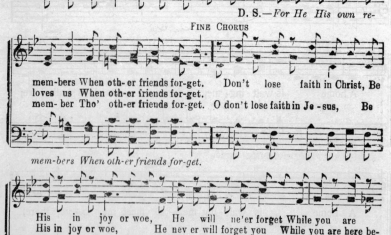

1. When all your friends forsake you And on a-lone you plod, Don't
2. Sometimes the path is drear-y And bit-ter tear-drops flow, So
3. O on the judg-ment morn-ing I with the saved shall stand, Be-

yield to sin, or wor-ry, But still have faith in God; He's far the
of-ten we have heartaches As on thru life we go; But Je-sus
cause my precious Sav-ior Is hold-ing now my hand; And when we

tru-est help-er That you have ev-er met, And He your soul re-
nev-er leaves us When tri-als great are met, He cares for us and
meet in heav-en When life's bright sun has set, My Sav-ior will re-

D. S.—For He His own re-

FINE **CHORUS**

mem-bers When oth-er friends for-get. Don't lose faith in Christ, Be
loves us When oth-er friends for-get.
mem-ber Tho' oth-er friends for-get. O don't lose faith in Je-sus, Be

mem-bers When oth-er friends for-get.

His in joy or woe, He will ne'er forget While you are
His in joy or woe, He nev-er will forget you While you are here be-

Jesus Remembers When Others Forget

here be-low; Tho' the world for-sake, He will be faith-ful yet,
low; tho' all the world forsake you,

No. 130   Shake Hands With Mother Again

W. A. B.   E. M. Bartlett, Owner   W. A. BERRY

1. If I should be liv-ing when Je-sus comes And could know the day
2. I'd like to say "Mo-ther, this is your boy, You left when you
3. There's com-ing a time when I can go home To meet my
4. There'll be no more sor-row or pain to bear In that home be-

and the hour, I'd like to be stand-ing at moth-er's tomb
went a-way; And now my dear moth-er it gives me great joy
loved-ones up there; There I can see Je-sus up-on His throne
yond the sky; Oh glo-ri-ous tho't when we all get there,

FINE   REFRAIN

When Je-sus comes in His pow'r.
To see you a-gain to-day." 'Twill be a won-der-ful hap-py day
In that bright ci-ty so fair.
We nev-er will say "good-by."

D.S.—"Shake hands with mother a-gain."

D. S.

Up there on the gold-en strand; When I can hear Je-sus my Sav-ior say,

No. 131   A Child at Mother's Knee

MISS ADA POWELL

AUSTIN HAZELWOOD

1. I'd like to wan-der back a-gain to days of long a-go,
2. I'd like to wan-der back to child-hood joys up-on the farm,
3. I'd like to be a child a-gain with-in the walls of home,
4. I'd like to kneel be-side my bed and to my Fa-ther pray,

To sit with-in the cir-cle there and watch the fire-light glow
And feel that I was safe a-gain from ev-'ry pass-ing harm,
And live in peace and hap-pi-ness, nor wish to stray or roam,
And trust to Him my wish-es in the old-time child-ish way,

Up-on fa-mil-iar fac-es of the ones I used to know;
Se-cure a-gainst all fol-lies and temp-ta-tion's lur-ing charm,
For tho' I climb o'er mountains grand or sail the ocean's foam,
For He is still my Fa-ther, and I hear Him gen-tly say,

I'd like to lis-ten to their foot-steps pass-ing to and fro.
And rest a-gain with-in the shel-ter of my moth-er's arm.
I'll nev-er find, in all this world, my moth-er or my home.
That He will ev-er guide and guard His child by night or day.

REFRAIN

I'd like to be (a lit-tle child) a-gain at moth-er's knee, I'd like to

Tennessee Music & Printing Co., owner

A Child at Mother's Knee

hear_____ her words of sym-pa-thy, I'd like to feel_____
Listen to her words of lov-ing   her loving arms

her arms en-cir-cle me, I'd like to be a child at mother's knee.
a-gain

No. 132   Precious Memories

J. B. F. W.

Stamps and Baxter, owners

J. B. F. Wright

1. Pre-cious mem'ries, un-seen an-gels, Sent from somewhere to my soul;
2. Pre-cious fa-ther, lov-ing mother, Fly a-cross the lone-ly years;
3. In the still-ness of the midnight, Ech-oes from the past I hear;
4. As I trav-el on life's pathway, Know not what the years may hold;

FINE

How they lin-ger, ev-er near me, And the sa-cred past un-fold.
And old home scenes of my childhood, In fond mem-o-ry ap-pears.
Old-time sing-ing, glad-ness bringing, From that lovely land somewhere.
As I pon-der, hope grows fonder, Pre-cious mem'ries flood my soul.

D. S.—*In the still-ness of the midnight, Pre-cious, sa-cred scenes unfold.*

CHORUS

D. S.

Pre-cious mem'ries, how they linger, How they ev-er flood my soul,

Old-Time Religion for Me

R. J. W. Copyright, 1930, by The Stamps-Baxter Music Co. R. J. Weaver

1. If I could on - ly wan-der back to the old camp meeting place, And
2. Ah, well do I re-mem-ber how the preach-er used to pray, And
3. I've nev - er lost the joy I had when Je - sus saved my soul, O

hear some brother, sis-ter tell of Christ and sav-ing grace; And hear that con-gre-
how he told the sto-ry in the good old fashioned way; O give me back those
how the tho't now thrills me that some day I'll reach the goal; I'll nev - er cease to

ga - tion sing so hap-py, glad and free, 'Tis the old time re - li - gion for me.
hap-py days, those days that used to be, 'Tis the old time re - li - gion for me.
love my Lord, He died on Cal-va-ry, 'Tis the old time re - li - gion for me.

CHORUS

'Tis the old time re - li - gion, (that saved me,) 'Tis the old time re-
(old time re- li-gion,)

li-gion, (sweet mem'ry,) 'Tis the old time re - li - gion for me;
(old time re - li-gion,) for me;

Old-Time Religion for Me

When our fa - thers were singing, (praise Je - sus,) And our
(it will take us all to heav-en,)

mothers were shouting (hal-le-lu-jah,)'Tis the old-time re-li-gion for me. (for me.)
(a - men,)

No. 134   Someone Rescued Me

Copyright, 1930, by The Stamps-Baxter Music Co.

B. B. E.   Rev. B. B. Edmiaston

1. Once I wandered from the Lord, Making sin of lib-er-ty; Blindly choosing endless
2. I was helpless in my sin, Mercy's face I could not see, Precious hope had turned a-
3. Now I owe to all a debt, I must help to make men free; It became my own, to
4. That the Father's kingdom come, From my sin He made me free; I will help the world to

FINE   CHORUS

death, But someone rescued me.   Someone rescued me,   And now in Christ I'm
way, Till someone rescued me.
pay, When someone rescued me.
win, Since someone rescued me.   rescued me,

D. S.–Since someone rescued me.

D. S.

free;(indeed I'm free;) I will tell the joy-ful news, helping others life to choose,

Keep Your Eyes Upon the Cross

Copyright, 1935, by The Stamps-Baxter Music Co.,
in "Harbor Bells No. 4"

A. G. Godley   J. O. Bearden

1. As you trav-el on the rug-ged road that leads to that home a-bove,
2. Je-sus promised that if we would al-ways to Him be whol-ly true,
3. Je-sus walked a-long the thorn-y road that we might be free in-deed,

Keep your eyes up-on the bless-ed cross that makes all men free; (so free;)
That He would not let the tempter cause us from Him to stray; (to stray;)
With a cross up-on His sin-less shoulders, suf-fered for thee; (for thee;)

Watch your step and nev-er let the temp-ter cause you to cease to love,
Walk close to Him, nev-er step a-side, but trust Him for He loves you,
What great love to bleed and die for men, sup-ply-ing our ev-'ry need,

Look to the Lamb who was slain for you on Cal-va-ry.
Then when you come to the stream of death He'll light the way.
For you and me there He bled and died on Cal-va-ry. Then keep your

CHORUS

Ev-er keep your eyes up-on the cru-el rug-ged cross,
eyes   up-on   the cross,............ Where Je-sus

Keep Your Eyes Upon the Cross

Where the Sav-ior bore our loss;............... Re - mem - ber,
bore   our shame and   free - ly bore our loss;

O re-mem-ber when the bil-lows 'round you fiercely toss, And keep your
Him   when bil - - lows toss,..................

rit.

eyes on the cross where He bled and died, look to the   cross.
                                                    sav - ing cross.

No. 136 Jesus Understands

Copyright, 1935, by The Stamps-Baxter Music Co.,
in "Harbor Bells No 4"

J. R. B., Jr.   J. R. Baxter. Jr.

1. When your heart is bleed-ing, Je-sus understands; When for help you're pleading,
2. When the darkness blinds you, Jesus understands; When a fet-ter binds you,
3. When a friend for-sakes you, Je-sus understands; When death's gloom o'er-takes you,

D. S.—He has gone be-fore you,

D. S.

FINE   **CHORUS**

Je - sus un - der - stands. Je - sus un - der - stands, Je - sus un - der - stands;

Je - sus un-der-stands.

No. 137 — The Lord Is With Me

LUTHER G. PRESLEY   ERNEST RIPPETOE

Not too fast

1. I live in a land of sor - row While toiling in this earth-ly race,
2. What-ev-er may be be-fore me I'll ev - er trust the Lord a - bove,
3. I'll trust till this race is end - ed, The tri - als of this life are past,

True joy is a - wait - ing yon-der Pre-pared for all the saved by grace;
So glad to be in His keep-ing, Safe shel-tered by His precious love;
And then I'll go home to glo - ry To dwell with all the saints at last;

The Sav - ior who bought my par - don Has gone those man-sions to pre - pare,
I want to be al - ways read - y My du - ty in this world to do,
What - ev - er may be my sor - row, The trou-ble that I here must bear,

Some hap - py day He will call me The glo - ry of that home to share.
That I may go home at ev'-ning The beau-ty of that land to view.
Each day I am in His keep-ing The glo - ry of His love to share.

Chorus

He is with me here   Ev - 'ry pass-ing day,
I know the Lord is with me Each mo-ment of the day,.......

The Lord Is With Me

I know that He   He will lead and cheer,   will lead me Tho   Dark may be the way;   dark may be   the way;

I know that in   Know this Christ of mine   each tri - al, He   Tra - vels on be-fore,   trav-els on   be-fore,........

And in His love   There is joy di - vine,   there's safe-ty, I   Could not ask for more.   could not ask   for more........

No. 138   I'm Nearing Home

Copyright, 1937, by The Stamps-Baxter Music Co.,
in "Harbor Bells No. 6"

J. W. EDWARDS   VAN B. CAGLE

1. I have a home in glo - ry, 'Tis ev - 'ry thing to me, I love to tell
2. A home of fade-less beau-ty, The streets are paved with gold; There I shall live
3. O won't you come and join me, And live for - ev - er there A-mong the friends

D. S.—That home He's built for me;   And by His grace

FINE   CHORUS   D.S.

the sto - ry, As sim - ple as can be.
with Je-sus And sing of love un-told.   I'm near-ing home, I'm near-ing home,
and loved ones And with the an-gels fair?

I'm go - ing To live e - ter - nal-ly.

Just a Little Talk with Jesus

SPIRITUAL

Copyright, 1937, by The Stamps-Baxter Music Co.,
in "Harbor Bells No. 6"

C. D.   CLEAVANT DERRICKS

1. I once was lost in sin but Je-sus took me in, And then a lit-tle
2. Sometimes my path seems drear, without a ray of cheer, And then a cloud of
3. I may have doubts and fears, my eyes be filled with tears, But Je-sus is a

light from heaven filled my soul; It bathed my heart in love and wrote my
doubt may hide the light of day; The mists of sin may rise and hide the
friend who watches day and night; I go to Him in pray'r, He knows my

name a-bove, And just a lit-tle talk with Je-sus made me whole......
star-ry skies, But just a lit-tle talk with Je-sus clears the way......
ev-'ry care, And just a lit-tle talk with Je-sus makes it right......

CHORUS

Have a lit-tle talk with Je-sus tell Him all a-bout our
Now let us   let us

trou-bles, Hear our faint-est cry an-swer by and by;
He will   and He will

Just a Little Talk with Jesus

Feel a lit - tle pray'r wheel turning, . know a lit - tle fire is

Now when you and you

burn-ing, Find a lit - tle talk with Jesus makes it right..............

You will it makes it right.

I Am Going

J. W. KEELE

1. There's a man - sion up in heav-en.......... In that bright....e-ter-nal
2. I am on......my way to glo - ry.......... And it won't......be ver - y
3. When my earth - ly work is end-ed.......... I shall go....to that glad

D.S.—When my Sav - ior calls for

land,.......... I am go - ing some glad morning.......... There to
long.......... Till I reach.....the shin-ing por-tals.... .... Of that
shore.......... There to live.....with friends now waiting,...... When we

me,.......... And I know......up there in glo - ry.......... I shall

FINE   CHORUS

join.... the an-gel band........ I am go - ing up to heav-en........
land.... of hap-py song........
meet... we'll part more........   I am go-ing   up to heaven

spend...e - ter - ni - ty.

Give the World a Smile

Otis Deaton

M. L. Yandell

1. Are you giv-ing to the world a smile, (sun-ny smile,) Help-ing
2. You may be a shin-ing light to-day, (yes, to-day,) Point-ing
3. Just a bright and sun-ny smile will win, (it will win,) Ma-ny

les-sen some ones drear-y mile? (drear-y mile?) Do you
souls to heav-en's glo-ry-way, (glo-ry-way,) If you
souls from drear-y paths of sin, (paths of sin,) Lift them

greet the world with song as thru life you pass a-long, Cheer-ing
let your light so shine that they see the path di-vine, And you
up on high-er plains, where they hear the glad re-frains Of the

REFRAIN

those whom you may meet a-long life's way? Give the
wear a pleas-ant smile a-long life's way. Give the world a
smil-ing band of work-ers on life's way. Give the world a

world a bright smile ev-'ry day, Help-ing some-one
smile each day, Help-ing some-one on life's

Give the World a Smile

on life's drear-y way; paths of sin bring them in,
way; From the paths of sin bring the wan-d'rers in,

To His fold, yes, for-ev-er to stay; Help to cheer
To the Mas-ter's fold to stay; Help

the lone and sad, Help to make some pil-grim
cheer the sad, the lone-ly and sad, Help make him glad,
the lone, the lone and sad, Help to make some wea-ry

glad, Let your life so be that all the world may
make somebod-y glad, life so be that
pil-grim glad,

see The joy of serv-ing Je-sus with a smile.
a bright sun-ny smile.

No. 142 Drifting Along

MRS. CHRISTINE S. BEVERIDGE in "Harbor Bells No. 6"   V. O. FOSSETT

1. Soul you are drift-ing a-long on the tide, Out on life's o - cean so
2. Drift-ing a - long with a smile and a song, Nev- er once thinking that
3. Why are you drift-ing a-long as be-fore, Tho't-less-ly down to e-

boundless and wide; Drifting a-way in the morning so bright, Where will you
you might be wrong; Morning has changed to the noon-tide's red glare, Still you are
ter - ni-ty's shore? Noon-day has passed, comes the set of life's sun, Where are you

CHORUS

be when you an-chor at night? Drift-ing a-long,   drifting a-long,
drift-ing, but an-swer me where?
now, when your drifting is done? Drift - ing a - long ...... With a

Smile and a song,   smile and a song, Drifting at night,   drifting at night,
smile .... and a song, ... Drift - ing at night, ...

In morning's light,   in morning's light; Drifting a-way,
And in morn's ...... gold-en light; .....   Drift - - - ing a-

Drifting Along

drifting a-way, Breakers now roar, breakers now roar, Drift -
way....... Where the break - ers now roar, ... Drifting to-day,

ing to-day .... From the beau - ti - ful gold - en shore.
drift-ing to - day, peace-ful shore.

No. 143   Come While He's Pleading

Copyright, 1937, by The Stamps-Baxter Music Co.,

J R. BAXTER, JR.   in "Harbor Bells No. 6"   R. L. STUCKEY

1. Come to the Sav-ior, win grace and fa-vor, He'll cleanse your sin-stained soul,
2. Come for a bless-ing, all now con-fess-ing, You will be glad you came;
3. Why stand de - bat-ing when He is wait-ing For you to ope the door?

FINE

Trusting Him ev - er, doubting Him nev - er, Bur-dens from you He'll roll.
He will re - ceive you, from sin re - lieve you, Then you can praise His name.
Bid Him now en - ter, hope on Him cen - ter, You will the Lord a - dore.

D.S.-Night shades are falling, list to His call-ing, Come and be - fore Him bow.

CHORUS   D. S.

Come while He's pleading, for you in - ter-ced - ing, He waits to save you now;

WE'LL REAP WHAT WE SOW.

JAMES ROWE.   WALTER B. SEALE.

1. Oh, let us be care-ful while sow-ing our seed, While toil-ing for
2. If naught to the world we are giv-ing to-day, Then noth-ing the
3. Sow on-ly our best for our heav-en-ly King, And then, when no

Je - sus be - low; Sow on - ly the things that the spir - it will need,
world will re - turn, But if we are serv-ing the Lord, on the way,
long - er we roam, The song of the reap-ers we ev - er shall sing,

FINE. CHORUS.

We'll reap what-so-ev - er we sow.
The life - crown we sure - ly shall earn. We'll reap what-so-ev -
At rest in our glo - ri - ous home.

D. S. We'll reap what - so - ev - er we sow.

We'll reap what we sow,
er we sow,............... What-ev - er the seeds they will

D. S.

Sure - ly will grow; Be care - ful in - deed, Sow on - ly good seed,
grow;

Mother and Home

Arr. copyright, 1937, by The Stamps-Baxter Music Co.

Words and music by W. J. LANEY

With feeling

1. Years a-go when just a boy, Singing songs was mother's joy, When my fath-er dear would
2. Fath-er was so good and kind, Oft he told us we would find, Not an-oth-er that would
3. Now I'm here so far a-way, From that home I've gone astray, Yet my moth-er oft-en

leave us there so lone, I can hear her voice so sweet, As she'd sing "When shall we meet:"
share our ills and woes;'Twas her hand that press'd my brow, I can al-most feel them now,
prays for me a-lone; Troubles, tri-als to en-dure, Yet I'll live a life that's pure,

CHORUS

I can ne'er for-get my mother and my home.
I can ne'er for-get my mother and my home. My dear mother was so true To her
Then I'll meet my dear sweet mother in our home.

children and her home; She was pa-tient, ten-der, kind and loved us all; I praise God for her sweet

rit.

name, She was ev-er just the same; I can ne'er for-get my moth-er and my home.

No. 146 Our Circle There

L. G. P.
Copyright, 1937, by The Stamps-Baxter Music Co.,
in "Harbor Bells No. 6"
LUTHER G. PRESLEY

1. I think of the cir-cle of the friends I have known, As fond-ly I
2. I know you have helped me when I need-ed a friend, So oft-en the
3. It's not e-nough glo-ry just to reach that sweet home, I want all my

cher-ish our friend-ship so true; How oft-en I won-der when this
right way to me you did show; That's why I'm ex-pect-ing when this
kin-dred and friends to be there; To join in the sing-ing 'neath the

earth life has flown, If we'll meet in that ci-ty just o-ver the blue.
life here shall end, I will meet you up yon-der where all the true go.
bright starry dome, With the ransomed for-ev-er His glo-ry to share.

CHORUS

Will the cir-cle.......... be un-brok-en.......... In the
Cir-cle be un-brok-en, cir-cle be un-brok-en,

sweet.......... by and by?.......... Find you there in glo-ry,
Sweet by and by, sweet by and by? Shall I find you........

Our Circle There

find you there in glory, When they call me to live there on high?
there in glo-ry......... When they call me to live there on high?........

I would have you....... for my neighbor,.......... In a
Have you for my neighbor, have you for my neighbor,

pal - - ace so fair,.......... Glad harps ring a welcome,
Pal-ace so fair, pal-ace so fair, Where the glad harps ...... ring a

glad harps ring a welcome, Will the cir - cle be un-brok-en there?........
wel-come,........ un-broken there?

No. 147. I Hope to Meet You By and By

J. R. B., JR.   J. R. BAXTER, JR.

1. There's a golden ci - ty In the sky, Where I hope to meet you By and by.
2. When we lose our burden On that day, Shall we meet in heaven There to stay?
3. Thru the countless ages Shall we be Sing-ing happy prais-es, Glad and free?

No. 148 He Wills It So

L. G. P.   Luther G. Presley

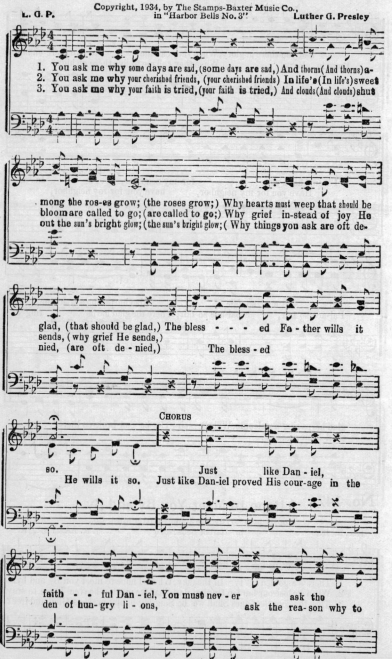

1. You ask me why some days are sad, (some days are sad,) And thorns (And thorns) a-
2. You ask me why your cherished friends, (your cherished friends) In life's (In life's) sweet
3. You ask me why your faith is tried, (your faith is tried,) And clouds (And clouds) shut

mong the ros-es grow; (the roses grow;) Why hearts must weep that should be
bloom are called to go; (are called to go;) Why grief in-stead of joy He
out the sun's bright glow; (the sun's bright glow; (Why things you ask are oft de-

glad, (that should be glad,) The bless - - - ed Fa-ther wills it
sends, (why grief He sends,)
nied, (are oft de-nied,) The bless - ed

CHORUS

so.   Just   like Dan - iel,
He wills it so. Just like Dan-iel proved His cour-age in the

faith - - ful Dan - iel, You must nev - er   ask the
den of hun-gry li - ons,   ask the rea-son why to

He Wills It So

reason **why to** know; Like the chil-dren, He - brew
know; Like the Hebrew children when they cast them in the fi - ery

children, Un-dis-mayed, He wills it so.
fur-nace, be not a-fraid, He wills it so.

No. 149   When Jesus Comes Back Again

C. W. T.   B. W. Tidwell

1. A time is appearing, we know not the day, When Jesus is com-ing in
2. O how will you meet Him when He shall appear? He sure- ly is com-ing, the
3. If you would live al-ways in mansions a-bove, Ac-cept His sal-va-tion, the

D. S.—*When Jesus comes back to the*

bright ar- ray; No more we shall suffer from sorrow and pain, When Jesus
time is near; Pray now for His mercy, 'twill then be in vain, When Jesus
gift of love; If cleansed from all sin you in heaven shall reign, When Jesus

earth a-gain; If free from all sin you in heaven shall reign, When Je-sus

FINE   CHORUS   D. S.

shall come back to the earth a-gain. When Jesus comes back a-gain,.........
to earth a - gain,

shall come back to the earth a-gain.

No. 150 I'll Meet You In The Morning

Respectfully dedicated to my wife, Goldie, and my sons,
Billey Joe, Albert E. Jr. and Thomas Rexton—A. E. B.
Copyright 1936 by Hartford Music Co. in "Lights of Life"   Albert E. Brumley

A. E. B.

1. I will meet you in the morn-ing, by the bright riv-er side,
2. I will meet you in the morn-ing, in the sweet by and by,
3. I will meet you in the morn-ing, at the end of the way,

When all sor-row has drift-ed a-way; I'll be standing at the
And exchange the old cross for a crown; There will be no dis-ap-
On the streets of that cit-y of gold; Where we all can be to-

port-als, when the gates o-pen wide, At the close of life's long, dreary day.
pointments and no-bod-y shall die, In that land, e'er the sun go-eth down.
geth-er and be hap-py for aye, While the years and the a-ges shall roll.

Chorus

I'll meet............... you in the morn-ing...............
meet you in the morn-ing,   meet you in the morn-ing,

with a "How............ do you do"............. and we'll
"How do you do"   "How do you do"

I'll Meet You In The Morning

sit down.............. by the riv - er................ and with
sit down by the riv - er   sit down by the riv - er

rap-ture "auld" acquaintance re - new,.......... You'll know............
rap-ture   our "auld" acquaintance re-new,   know me in the morn-

me in the morn-ing,............... by the smiles.......... that I
ing,   know me in the morn-ing,   smiles that I wear

wear,.........when I meet you........... in the morning,...........
smiles that I wear,   meet you in the morning,   meet you in the morning,

In the cit - y that is built   four square..............
cit - y   cit - y built, that cit - y built four square.

No. 151   I Hold His Hand

J. R. Baxter, Jr.   Copyright, 1929, by W. A. Sims and J. R. Baxter, Jr.   **W. Allen Sims**

1. I hold to the hand of my Savior and friend, He shields me from evil till
2. I hold to His hand when the storm-clouds a-rise, He speaks and the shadows roll
3. I hold to the hand that is steadfast and sure, No oth-er foun-da-tion is

dan-gers all end, He'll take me to heaven where voices now blend; I hold to the
back from the skies, 'Tis wonderful glo-ry for our human eyes; I hold to the
ev - er se-cure, I look for the home that will ev-er en-dure; I hold to the

REFRAIN

hand of my Lord.   Dai-ly I hold   to the scarred hand
I hold.......... to the hand   of my

of my dear Lord,   Sav - ior and King,   Till I am safe
Sav - - ior and King,.......... Till safe............ in that

in that glad home,   an - gels of God   prais-es now sing; He
cit - - y where an - - gels now sing;..........

I Hold His Hand

leads........ me so gent - ly where still...... wa-ters flow,......
Ev - er He leads gently a - long where sparkling pure, still waters flow,

And tells........ me of heav - en where I long to go......
Tells me of love, heaven above where I ev-er long, yes, I long to go.

No. 152   Holy Manna

Baptist Harmony   Arr.

1. Breth-ren, we have met to wor - ship And a - dore the Lord, our God;
2. Breth-ren, see poor sin - ners 'round you, Slumb'ring on the brink of woe;
3. Sis - ters, will you join and help us, While we strug-gle hard with sin;
4. Let us love our God su - preme-ly, Let us love each oth - er, too;

Will you pray with all your pow - er, While we try to preach the Word?
Death is com-ing, hell is mov-ing, Can you bear to let them go?
Will you tell to trem-bling mourners, Je - sus waits to wel-come them?
Let us love and pray for sin-ners, Till our God makes all things new.

D. S.—*Brethren, pray that ho - ly man-na May be showered all a- round.*

REFRAIN   D. S.

All is vain, un - less the Spir - it Of the Ho - ly One comes down;

No. 153 — When Jesus Comes

R. B. Taylor

M. L. Yandell

1. A few more years may pass a - way, A few more years to watch and pray;
2. He bled and died up - on the cross, He suf - fered there to save the lost;
3. In fan - cy I can see Him now, As I in deep con - tri - tion bow;

Then Je - sus shall from heaven's dome Come down to earth and claim His own.
And bids us yet a - while re - main On earth till He shall come a - gain.
He's com - ing with His an - gel band To take me to the prom - ised land.

CHORUS

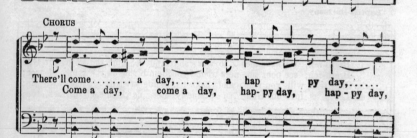

There'll come........ a day,........ a hap - py day,......
Come a day, come a day, hap- py day, hap - py day,

When we........ on wings...... will soar...... a - way;......
We on wings, lov- ing wings Soar a - way, far a - way;

Where heav - en's bells...... will sweet - ly chime,....
Heaven's bells, heaven's bells sweet-ly chime, sweet-ly chime,

When Jesus Comes

O won't that be a happy time When Christ our Lord shall come.... shall come.

No. 154   I Shall Live With Jesus

Arr. by O. C. F.   O. C. Fulkerson, owner   O. C. Fulkerson

1. When this bu - sy life is end - ed, And my race on earth is run;
2. When the sun goes down for - ev - er. Moon and stars have ceased to be,
3. O Thou pre - cious lov - ing Fa - ther, Guide my foot-steps day by day,

I shall lay a - side my bur - den At the set - ting of the sun.
With the dawn of judg-ment morn-ing, Take me home to live with Thee.
Then with all my jour-ney end - ed, Let me live with Thee for aye.

REFRAIN

I shall go to live with Je - sus, In bright mansions up a - bove,

rit.

There to sing His praise in glo - ry, Saved by His re-deem-ing love.

My Savior

J. R. B., Jr.   Arr. by J. R. Baxter, Jr.

Slow

1. My soul was drift-ing far from the road, No friend was lift-ing
2. Sin had me cling-ing as by a thread, Each day was bring-ing
3. Each friend-ly warn-ing I did not heed, My soul was scorn-ing

my heav-y load; Con-stant-ly shift-ing, found no a-bode,
noth-ing but dread; Death knells were ring-ing o-ver my head,
Him who could lead; Noon, night and morn-ing I felt the need,

Chorus

Till un-to Christ I called. Je-sus then heard my
Je-sus Christ then quick-ly heard my

Christ heard

cry of sad-ness, Gave me the joy for which my
fee-ble cry of grief and sad-ness, Gave

my cry of sad-ness

soul so long had craved; He changed my
I am hap-py, I am hap-py; O He changed my

and I am free and hap-py; Changed

My Savior

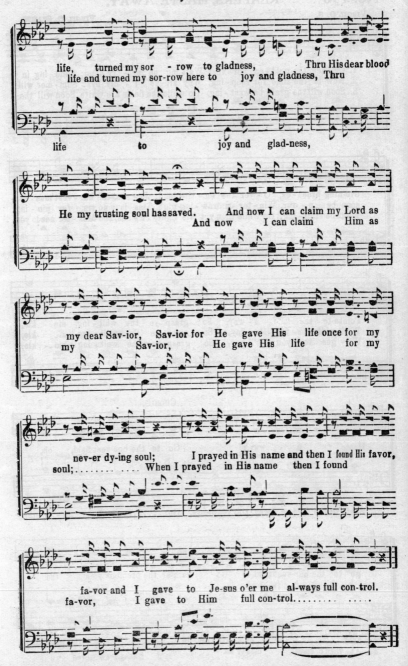

No. 156 REAPERS, HASTE AWAY.

Virgil O. S.

Virgil O. Stamps

1. Oh see the gold-en har-vest Wait-ing on ev-'ry hand; Bend-ing in
2. Now is the time for reap-ing, Why sit ye i-dly by? Sum-mer will
3. Soon will the grain be wast-ing, Go while the fields are white, Soon will the

eve-ning breez-es, O-ver the en-tire land; Je-sus, the har-vest mas-ter,
soon be o-ver, Win-ter is draw-ing nigh, This is no time for pin-ing,
night be fall-ing, Go while then yet 'tis light; Je-sus, the Mas-ter needs you,

Points to the field a-way, So grasp ye the wait-ing sic-kle,
Work while it yet is day, So grasp ye the wait-ing sic-kle,
Wa-ges to you He'll pay, So grasp ye the wait-ing sic-kle,

CHORUS.

Haste a-way. Go to the har-vest field, oh,

Haste to the field a-way, oh reap-ers. Go................. in-to the

go to the har-vest field, Go gath-er the precious yield, the

field.............. and gath-er in.................. the pre-cious

REAPERS, HASTE AWAY.

No. 157   I Am O'ershadowed by Love

J. R. Baxter, Jr.   Copyright, 1929, by O. V. Grice and J. R. Baxter, Jr.   O. V. Grice

1. All a-round me ev-'ry mo-ment is the won-drous love of God,
2. I can tread the pil-grim jour-ney know-ing love is help-ing me,
3. Friend you ought to know the pleas-ure that His love to me now gives,

Thrill-ing my soul, keep-ing me whole; And it lights the path to
Thrill-ing my soul, keep-ing me whole; I shall still be march-ing
Thrill-ing my soul, keep-ing me whole; I shall share His joy and

glo-ry, show-ing where the Mas-ter trod, I am o'er-shadowed by love.
on-ward till that cit-y I shall see, I am o'er-shadowed by love
glo-ry where the soul for-ev-er lives, I am o'er-shadowed by love.

Refrain

by God's won-drous, His mar-vel-ous love,
O'ershadowed by God's wondrous love,............ I'm on my

way to realms up in heav-en a-bove; reach that home so
way to realms a-bove;............ And when I reach that home so

I Am O'ershadowed by Love

ex-ceed-ing-ly fair, still be with me, 'twill be with me there.
fair, ... His love will still be with me there . . . .

No. 158   Jesus Keeps Me Singing

Copyright, 1931, by The Stamps-Baxter Music Co.,
in "Tuneful Praise"

E. W. Tidwell.   D. W. Whaley

1. Je - sus keeps a car - ol ring-ing in my soul As I jour-ney to my
2. Once when I was wand'ring, wasting precious time, Je-sus came and res-cued
3. Oft when I am lone - ly and the way seems dim, There's no one to help me

home a-bove,   Prais-es I am voic-ing, fac-ing heav-en's goal, Sing-ing
me from sin;   Now my soul is hap - py in His love sub-lime, Sing-ing
with a song;   Je - sus calls me near-er and I walk with Him, Prais-ing

D. S. — *Trib-utes to Him bringing on the homeward way, Sing-ing*

FINE   **CHORUS**

of re-deem-ing love . . . . .   Je-sus keeps me sing-ing   on my
helps my soul to win . . . . .   singing, singing on my
Him the whole day long . . . .

of re-deem-ing love . . . . .   D. S.

way,   Keeps the joy-bells ringing   ev - 'ry day;
way, (to glo-ry,)   ringing, ringing ev-'ry day; (true story;)

No. 159 Till He Calls His Reapers

O. A. Parris

The V. O. Stamps Music Co., owners

J. D. Wall

1. In the har-vest we should be reaping, For we have no time to be sleeping,
2. Man-y souls a-round us are dy-ing, While the precious moments are fly-ing,
3. While we work the Master will bless us, In His arms He'll take and caress us,

And we ev-er should plod; No re-ward is giv-en to shirk-ers,
Broth-er, an-swer the call; While the day of mer-cy is giv-en
Giv-ing comfort and love; As to Him glad sheaves we are bring-ing,

Ev-'ry one should be a true worker In the harvest of God. We'll be true,
Seek the lost and point them to heaven, There is mercy for all.
We'll be true and ev-er keep singing, Till He calls us a-bove. We'll be

CHORUS

ev-er true, All the way, All the way, And
we'll be ev-er true, Pilgrim journey thru, yes, All the pil-grim way,
true The jour - ney thru.

from the fold we will not roam, But we will work and sing, For
We will work, we will work and sing

Till He Calls His Reapers

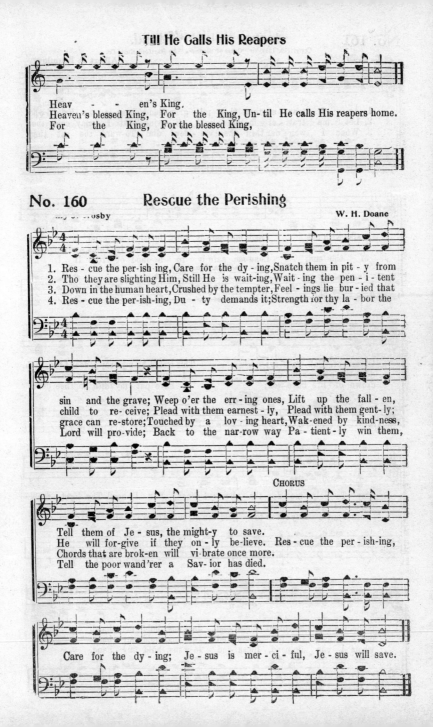

Heav - - en's King.
Heaven's blessed King, For the King, Un-til He calls His reapers home.
For the King, For the blessed King,

No. 160 Rescue the Perishing

W. H. Doane

1. Res - cue the per-ish-ing, Care for the dy - ing, Snatch them in pit - y from
2. Tho they are slighting Him, Still He is wait-ing, Wait - ing the pen - i - tent
3. Down in the human heart, Crushed by the tempter, Feel - ings lie bur - ied that
4. Res - cue the per-ish-ing, Du - ty demands it; Strength for thy la - bor the

sin and the grave; Weep o'er the err - ing ones, Lift up the fall - en,
child to re - ceive; Plead with them earnest - ly, Plead with them gent - ly;
grace can re-store; Touched by a lov - ing heart, Wak-ened by kind-ness,
Lord will pro-vide; Back to the nar-row way Pa - tient-ly win them,

CHORUS

Tell them of Je - sus, the might-y to save.
He will for-give if they on - ly be-lieve. Res - cue the per - ish-ing,
Chords that are brok-en will vi-brate once more.
Tell the poor wand'rer a Sav - ior has died.

Care for the dy - ing; Je - sus is mer - ci - ful, Je - sus will save.

No. 161   Jesus, Hold My Hand.

A. E. B.   Albert E. Brumley.

1. As I trav-el thru this pil-grim land There is a Friend who walks with me, Leads me safe-ly thro' the sink-ing sand, It is the Christ of Cal-va-ry; This would be my pray'r, dear Lord, each day To help me do the best I can, For I need Thy light to guide me day and night Bless-ed Je-sus, hold my hand.

2. Let me trav-el in the light di-vine That I may see the bless-ed way; Keep me that I may be whol-ly Thine And sing re-demption's song some day; I will be a sol-dier brave and true And ev-er firm-ly take a stand, As I on-ward go and dai-ly meet the foe, Bless-ed Je-sus, hold my hand.

3. When I wan-der thru the val-ley dim To-ward the set-ting of the sun, Lead me safe-ly to a land of rest If I a crown of life have won; I have put my faith in Thee, dear Lord, That I may reach the gold-en strand, There's no oth-er friend on whom I can de-pend, Bless-ed Je-sus, hold my hand.

Jesus, Hold My Hand.

No. 162 Wonderful

James Rowe   The V. O. Stamps Music Co., owners.   M. L. Yandell

1. Won-der-ful is Je-sus, our matchless King, Wonder-ful the praise which to
2. Won-der-ful is Je-sus, who saves by grace, Wonder-ful the beau-ty of
3. Won-der-ful is Je-sus, who saves the soul, Wonder-ful is He who can

Him we sing; Won-der-ful the friend un-to whom we cling, On the way to
His dear face; So we seek with Him an a-bid-ing place, In the bless-ed
keep us whole; That is why we seek the e-ter-nal goal, In the wondrous

glo - ry - land.
glo - ry - land.
glo - ry - land.

CHORUS

Our Lord is lead-ing us to glo-ry, Oh, so

won-der-ful is He,   won-der-ful is He,
is our Sav-ior,   praise Him ev-er,

Won-der-ful is He,   Lead-ing us to realms of glo-ry,
Christ, the Sav-ior;

Sing-ing as we go,
out His won-drous sto - ry,
Mak-ing known the love that made us

free,
that made us free for-ev-er.
Won-der-ful sal - va-tion He is of - fer-ing

to all,
yes, our Lord is
of - fer-ing to all,
Free-ly He is
of - fer-ing to

all
who trust Him;
Won-der-ful is He who leads us lov-ing - ly a - bove,

Won-der - ful,
Won-der - ful,
Won-der - ful is He,
to me.

The Little White Church

C. P.

Chas. Pleasant

1. There's a lit-tle white church in the val-ley That stands in my mem-o-
2. They would sing the old song "Rock of A-ges" "O Christ, let me hide my-
3. And when I shall cross o'er that dark riv-er, The face of my Sav-ior

ry each day, And it seems I can hear the bell ring-ing, Tho' I am
self in Thee," And I know some of them are now wait-ing Just o'er the
I shall see, O I hope that they all will be sing-ing The song "Near-

man-y miles a-way; And man-y times on Sunday morning The whole country-
dark and stormy sea; I know their troubles all are end-ed And hap-py for-
er, my God, to Thee;" And when I en-ter that bright ci-ty, In splendor for-

side would gather there, They would all kneel down by the al-tar As they
ev-er they shall be, They are wait-ing, watching up yon-der For the
ev-er I shall dwell, And the fac-es there will be man-y From the

CHORUS

lift-ed up their voice in pray'r. O the church in the val-ley,
com-ing home of you and me.
lit-tle church down in the dell.

O the

The Little White Church

lit-tle white church, Place that I love so well: Sad and lone-ly,
'Tis the Now I'm

sad and lone-ly, For the lit - tle white church in the dell.....
yes, I'm

No. 164   Plant a Little Spark of Love

W. P. P.   W. P. Poteet, owner   W. P. Poteet

1. While I sail life's roll-ing sea,   When the waves are tossing me:
2. I have con-fi-dence in you,   You have been so kind and true;
3. Till this earth-ly life is o'er   And I an-chor on that shore,

FINE

Pray that I the light may see,....   Plant a lit - tle spark of love.....
Teach me things that I may do,...   Help me plant a spark of love....
Where I'll live for-ev - er-more..   Just keep planting sparks of love...

D. S.-*Till you meet the Heav'nly Dove,*   *Just keep planting sparks of love.*

CHORUS   D. S.

Plant a lit- tle spark of love,   Point lost souls to God a - bove;

No. 165 Tell Me Who is My Neighbor

Especially dedicated to all Odd Fellows and to all Christians who are traveling this road daily, may they never fail to emulate the example of the Good Samaritan.

E. F. F.   Copyright, 1934, by E. F. Fulmer   E. F. Fulmer

1. From Je-ru-sa-lem to Jer-i-cho, Up-on a lone-ly road,
2. From Je-ru-sa-lem to Jer-i-cho, A cer-tain Priest passed by,
3. From Je-ru-sa-lem to Jer-i-cho, A Le-vite came a-long,
4. From Je-ru-sa-lem to Jer-i-cho, As life was pass-ing 'way,
5. Tho' the Priests may pass a-long their way And Le-vites fol-low, too,

A cer-tain man was set up-on And robbed of all his gold;
He saw the poor man ly-ing there But heed-ed not his cry;
But heed-ing not the cry of him Who lay up-on the ground;
There came a lone Sa-mar-i-tan Who was de-spised, they say;
Un-mind-ful of the ho-ly work Which they were meant to do;

They kicked him and they beat him And left Him there for dead,
He caught his robes a-bout him And quick-ly he was gone,
He raised his head up high-er And quick-ly passed a-long,
He gent-ly raised the trav-'ler And took him to an inn,
We'll ne'er for-sake a broth-er, We'll aid both aged and youth,

Who was it then that came a-long And bathed His ach-ing head?
Who was it then that helped the man The rob-bers set up-on?
Who was it then that helped the man The rob-bers set up-on?
He paid the bill and asked the host To take good care of him.
A no-ble band we'll firm-ly stand For friend-ship, love and truth.

Tell Me Who is My Neighbor

CHORUS

Tell me who, tell me who, Who was
Tell me who, tell me who,

neigh-bor kind and true; Tell me who, tell me
kind and true; Tell me who,

who, A neigh-bor-ly deed did do?
tell me who, did do?

From Je-ru-sa-lem to Jer-i-cho, We're trav-'ling ev-'ry day,

And man-y are the dy-ing ones That lie a-long our way.

No. 166   Pictures From Life's Other Side

Arr. L. G. P.

Copyright, 1937, by The Stamps-Baxter Music Co.
in "Favorite Radio Songs"

J. B. VAUGHAN
Arr. LUTHER G. PRESLEY

1. This world's mag-ic gal'-ry of pic-tures   Are the scenes that are
2. The first was a scene of a gam-bler,   Who had lost all his
3. The next was a scene of two broth-ers   And their path-ways in
4. The next was a scene by the riv-er,   Of a heart-brok-en

paint-ed from life,   They are scenes of much grief and of pas-sion,   They are
mon-ey at play,   Drew his dead moth-er's ring from his finger,   That she
life a-part led,   One of them was in lux-u-ry liv-ing,   While the
moth-er and babe,   'Neath the harbor lights they stand and shiver,   On-ly

pic-tures of love and of strife;   The pic-tures of youth and of beau-ty,
wore on her glad wedding day;   His last earth-ly treasure, he stakes it,
oth-er one begged for his bread;   One dark night they met on the high-way,
out-casts whom no one would save;   And yet she was once a true wo-man—

Old age and the blush-ing young bride,   All hang on the wall, but the
And bows that his shame he might hide,   They lift-ed his head, but the
"Your mon-ey or life" the thief cried,   He then with his knife took his
Was some-bod-y's darl-ing and pride,   God help her, she leaps, there is

Pictures From Life's Other Side

FINE   CHORUS

sad - dest of all   Are the pictures from life's oth - er side.
gam - bler was dead, 'Tis   a   pic-ture from life's oth - er side.   'Tis a
own broth-er's life, 'Tis   a   pic-ture from life's oth - er side.
no   one who weeps, 'Tis   a   pic-ture from life's oth - er side.

D. S.—loved one so dear, 'Tis a pic-ture from life's oth - er side.

pic - - - ture from life's oth - er side, Some-bod-y who fell by the
Picture from life,   life's oth - er side,

way........, A life........ had gone out with the tide That might have been
by the way,   Life had gone out,   out with the tide

hap-py some day; ....   Moth - er is wait-ing,   wait-ing at home
been happy some day;Some moth - - - er is   wait-ing at home

D.S.

For the ships that come in with the tide,........ She is wait-ing to hear from a
on-rush-ing tide,

The Old Home Place

"Be it ever so humble, there's no place like home"

A. C. D.   A. C. Doss, owner   Albert C. Doss

1. There's an old home place that I would like to see, A smil-ing face now wait-ing
2. There's a low sweet voice, I seem to hear it now, As to her God so meek-ly
3. Just an old-time home and built so ver-y plain, Tho far I roam, I love it

there for me; I've a moth-er there to an-swer ev-'ry call, I'm think-ing of her
she did bow; There's a pray'r I can re-mem-ber ev-'ry day, It leads me in the
just the same; There's a winding trail, a light that I can see, I know some one is

CHORUS.

pic-ture on the wall.   I can hear   her voice so sweet,
straight and nar-row way.
wait-ing there for me.   I can hear....... her voice so sweet,

As she sang....... "when shall we meet;"   There's a wind-ing trail, a
As she sang   "when shall we meet;"

light that I can see, I know some one is wait-ing there for me.

Going Home

J. R. B., Jr.   J. R. Baxter, Jr.

1. I'm a pil-grim and a stranger in this wild-er-ness be-low, But I
2. I can nev - er tar - ry lon-ger than to rest my weary feet, For my
3. Ev - 'ry night-fall brings me nearer to the cit - y bright above, Where no

have a mansion o'er the foam; I must face sin's awful danger, watch for
goal is 'neath the heav'nly dome; With a faith that's growing stronger, I shall
more my feet shall ev - er roam; And the path is growing clear-er, I am

foot-prints as I go, When the race is o - ver, I am go - ing home.
nev - er taste defeat, When the race is o - ver, I am go - ing home.
trusting in God's love, When the race is o - ver, I am go - ing home.

CHORUS

Going home,...... go-ing home, ... It won't be long, it may be soon;
Going home,   going home,

Going home,...... going home, ...Some day I'm going home,....
Going home,   going home,   go-ing home.

Voices Are Calling.

1. S. T. Last two stanzas by N. W. Allphin.

Tillit S. Teddlie.

1. Oft when the twi-light gath-ers a-round me, Clear, in the shad-ows,
2. Friends of the past, whom oft-en I've greet-ed, Here as they jour-neyed,
3. Ma-ny are gone, who here were my kin-dred, To the a-bode of

fa-ces I see; Deep in the still-ness voic-es are call-ing,
ev-en as I; Lov-ing-ly wait and watch for my com-ing,
spir-its made free; They, with my Lord and all His redeemed ones.

CHORUS.

Loved ones are call-ing, call-ing for me.
With them to share the glo-ries on high. Sweet-ly they're call-ing,
Long-ing-ly wait and beck-on for me.

lov-ing-ly call-ing, Those whom I loved, so hap-py and free; Out from the

rit.

shin-ing por-tals of glo-ry, Loved ones are call-ing, call-ing for me.

There's A Crown For Your Cross

Miss Ada Powell   Austin Hazelwood, owner.   Used by per.   **Austin Hazelwood**

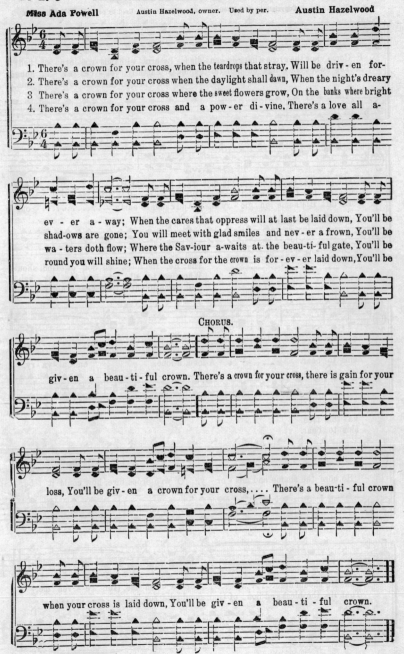

1. There's a crown for your cross, when the teardrops that stray, Will be driv-en for-
2. There's a crown for your cross when the daylight shall dawn, When the night's dreary
3. There's a crown for your cross where the sweet flowers grow, On the banks where bright
4. There's a crown for your cross and a pow-er di-vine, There's a love all a-

ev-er a-way; When the cares that oppress will at last be laid down, You'll be
shad-ows are gone; You will meet with glad smiles and nev-er a frown, You'll be
wa-ters doth flow; Where the Sav-iour a-waits at-the beau-ti-ful gate, You'll be
round you will shine; When the cross for the crown is for-ev-er laid down, You'll be

Chorus.

giv-en a beau-ti-ful crown. There's a crown for your cross, there is gain for your

loss, You'll be giv-en a crown for your cross,.... There's a beau-ti-ful crown

when your cross is laid down, You'll be giv-en a beau-ti-ful crown.

No. 171   Wondrous Love.

J. E. Franklin.   Copyright by J. E. Thomas. All rights reserved, Used by per.   J. E. Thomas.

1. Come view the cross where Je - sus died, By cru - el hands was cru - ci - fied;
2. The sweet-est song on mor-tal tongue, Or earth-ly voi - ces ev - er sung,
3. No oth - er One in heav'n-ly bliss Could e'er con-ceive a love like this;

O won-drous tho't, how could it be? That He should die.............. for
Is of the One on Cal - va - ry, Who gives to all. .... sal-
He left His home in glo - ry there And came to earth .... our

That He, the bless - ed Son of God, should
Who gives to all who hum-bly ask sal-
And came to earth from heav'n a-bove our

CHORUS.

e - ven me.   A-lone, a - lone,.......... on Cal - va - ry,............
va - tion free.
sins to bear.   A-lone, a-lone,   on Cal - va - ry,

die for me.
va - tion free.
sins to bear.

He bore the shame and mis - er - y,   O won-drous love, how could it be,

That He should die............. for e - ven me, (for e - ven me.)
That He, the bless - ed Son of God, should die for me..................

No. 172 From the Cross to the Crown

F. L. E.   Stamps-Baxter Music Co., owners   F. L. EILAND

1. Look a - way from the cross to the glit-ter-ing crown, From your cares weary
2. Tho' the bur - dens of life may be heav - y to bear, And your crosses and
3. 'Mid the con-flicts, the battles, the struggles and strife, Bravely onward your

one look a-way; There's a home for the soul, where no sor-row can come
tri - als se-vere; There's a beau - ti - ful hand that is beck-on-ing come
jour-ney pur-sue; Look a-way from the cross to the glit-ter-ing crown

CHORUS

And where pleasures will nev-er de-cay. Look a-way, look a-
And no heart-aches and sighings are there.
That's a-wait-ing in heav-en for you. Wea-ry one, look a-way from the

way, From the cross to the glit-ter-ing crown, Look a-
cross to the crown, glittering crown, Weary

way, look a - way, From the cross to the glittering crown.
one, look away from the cross to the crown,

No. 173 'Don't You Want To Be Ready.

"Therefore, be ye also ready."—MATT. 24: 44.

Copyright, 1895, by F. L. Eiland.

F. L. Eiland.

1. O there is a time when the message will come, Don't you want to be
2. To-day is the day of sal-va-tion for all, Can you say you are
3. O yes, there's a time when the message will come, Are you will-ing and

read-y to go? O sin-ner, the Sav-iour in-vites you to-day, Will you
read-y to go? A home and a crown is a-wait-ing for thee, Will you
read-y to go? This mo-ment the Sav-iour is pleading for thee, Sin-ner,

CHORUS.

hear and be ready to go? Read - y to go,
come and be ready to go?
say, are you ready to go? Watching and waiting and read-y to go, Don't you

1

Read - y to go, Don't you want to be read-y to
want to be wait-ing and read-y to go? yes,

2

go? go?..........Don't you want to be read-y to go?
read-y to go? read-y to go?

The Palace Of Prayer

Rev. B. B. Edmiaston

A. G. Godley

1. There's a won-der-ful life-giv-ing sto-ry, Of a pal-ace of beau-ty most rare; How the an-gels of peace come from glo-ry, Meet-ing us in the pal-ace of pray'r.
2. When con-fus-ion of earth would con-found me, When my spir-it is wea-ry with care, Heaven's qui-et comes gen-tly a-round me, When I en-ter the pal-ace of pray'r.
3. When the shad-ows of sor-row come o'er me, When my bur-dens are heav-y to bear, An-gel voic-es in mer-cy im-plore me, To en-ter the pal-ace of pray'r.
4. So I'll live near this pal-ace of bless-ing, To its courts I will of-ten re-pair; For I feel my dear Sav-ior's ca-ress-ing, In the beau-ti-ful pal-ace of pray'r.

CHORUS.

In the won-der-ful pal-ace of beau-ty,...... We may leave ev-'ry sor-row and care,....... And re-ceive a new vision of du-ty;....... Je-sus meets us in the pal-ace of pray'r.

and love, ev-'ry care, from a-bove;

dim. ad lib.

No. 175 Hold to God's Unchanging Hand

at enjoy, beyond expressing, That we have at our command,
Thus to know that we can ever Hold to God's unchanging hand.—F.L.E.

JENNIE WILSON   F. L. EILAND

1. Time is filled with swift transition,   Naught of earth unmoved can stand;
2. Trust in Him who will not leave you, What - so - ev - er years may bring;
3. Cov - et not this world's vain riches   That so rap - id - ly de - cay,
4. When your journey is com-plet - ed,   If to God you have been true;

Rit.

Build your hopes on things e - ter - nal,   Hold, to God's un-chang-ing hand.
If   by earth-ly friends for-sa - ken,   Still more close-ly to Him cling.
Seek   to gain the heav'nly treasures,   They will nev -er pass a - way.
Fair and bright the home in glo - ry,-   Your en-rap-tured soul will view.

Chorus

Hold........ to God's unchanging hand, Hold........to God's unchanging hand;
to His hand,   to His hand,

Rit.

Build your hopes on things e-ter - nal,   Hold to God's un-chang-ing hand.

No 176 BEAUTIFUL HOME SOMEWHERE.

J. B. V.

J. B. VAUGHAN.

DUET.

1. Oft-en I've heard of heav-en, won-der-ful coun-try some-where,
2. Oft-en we sing the sto-ry, beau-ti-ful sto-ry so sweet,
3. Oft-en I dream of glo-ry, vis-ions so love-ly and fair,

Beau-ti-ful sto-ry of glo-ry, land of de-light so fair;
Oft-en we hear of its glo-ry— where the re-deemed ones meet,
I am so hap-py in Je-sus, long-ing to be up there;

E-den, sweet home up yon-der, Je-sus has gone to pre-
Wait-ing till Je-sus calls me, then I shall rest with the
Bless-ed Re-deem-er's com-ing, then I shall go to that

pare us a home, Sweet home, I shall soon be there.
good and the blest, My glo-ry will be com-plete.
beau-ti-ful shore, For-ev-er at home some-where.

CHORUS.

Home o-ver yon - der, Beau-ti-ful home some-where,......
Home o-ver yon-der some-where, Won-der-ful home, my beau-ti-ful home,

Oh,............................... beau-ti-ful, beau-ti-ful
Beau-ti-ful, won-der-ful, beau-ti-ful home,

home,........... Some day I shall reach my sweet home.....
beau-ti-ful home, sweet home.

J. B. Vaughan, owner. Used by per.

No. 177. Everybody will be Happy Over There.

E. M. Bartlett.

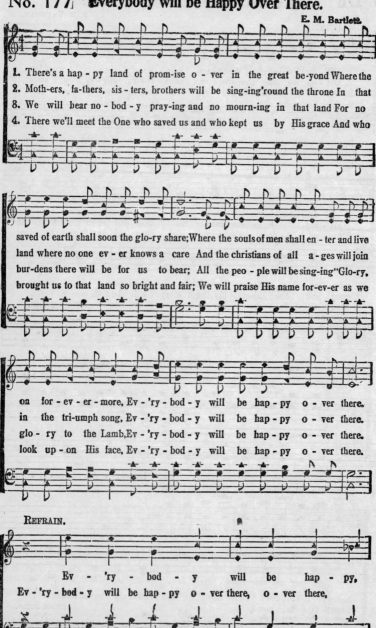

1. There's a hap-py land of prom-ise o-ver in the great be-yond Where the
2. Moth-ers, fa-thers, sis-ters, brothers will be sing-ing'round the throne In that
3. We will bear no-bod-y pray-ing and no mourn-ing in that land For no
4. There we'll meet the One who saved us and who kept us by His grace And who

saved of earth shall soon the glo-ry share; Where the souls of men shall en-ter and live
land where no one ev-er knows a care And the christians of all a-ges will join
bur-dens there will be for us to bear; All the peo-ple will be sing-ing "Glo-ry,
brought us to that land so bright and fair; We will praise His name for-ev-er as we

on for-ev-er-more, Ev-'ry-bod-y will be hap-py o-ver there.
in the tri-umph song, Ev-'ry-bod-y will be hap-py o-ver there.
glo-ry to the Lamb, Ev-'ry-bod-y will be hap-py o-ver there.
look up-on His face, Ev-'ry-bod-y will be hap-py o-ver there.

REFRAIN.

Ev-'ry-bod-y will be hap-py,
Ev-'ry-bod-y will be hap-py o-ver there, o-ver there,

Everybody Will Be Happy Over There.

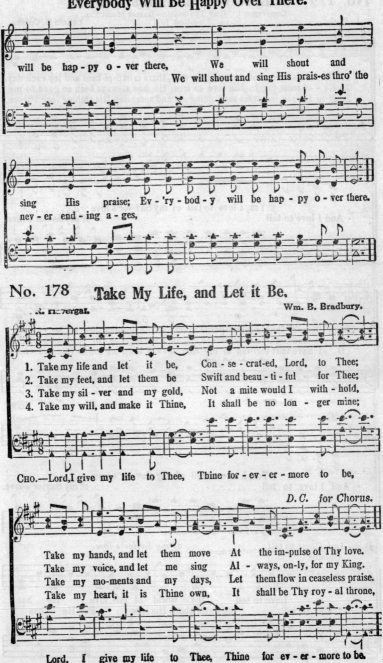

will be hap-py o-ver there, We will shout and
We will shout and sing His prais-es thro' the

sing His praise; Ev-'ry-bod-y will be hap-py o-ver there.
nev-er end-ing a-ges,

No. 178   Take My Life, and Let it Be.

F. R. Havergal.

Wm. B. Bradbury.

1. Take my life and let it be, Con-se-crat-ed, Lord, to Thee;
2. Take my feet, and let them be Swift and beau-ti-ful for Thee;
3. Take my sil-ver and my gold, Not a mite would I with-hold,
4. Take my will, and make it Thine, It shall be no lon-ger mine;

CHO.—Lord, I give my life to Thee, Thine for-ev-er-more to be,

D. C. for Chorus.

Take my hands, and let them move At the im-pulse of Thy love.
Take my voice, and let me sing Al-ways, on-ly, for my King.
Take my mo-ments and my days, Let them flow in ceaseless praise.
Take my heart, it is Thine own, It shall be Thy roy-al throne,

Lord, I give my life to Thee, Thine for ev-er-more to be.

No. 179 I Love to Tell of His Love

L. B. C.

Lonnie B. Combs

1. As I jour-ney on this pilgrim way, there is hap-pi-ness and joy each day,
2. Ev - er trust-ing in His love so free, He has al-ways been so good to me,
3. Now His lov-ing arms are holding me and some day His smiling face I'll see,

Yes, I love to tell of my Sav-ior's love;..............
And I love to tell.............. of my Savior's love;

Soon I'll reach that home prepared for me, I'll be sing-ing thru e - ter - ni - ty,
He is lead-ing me to realms so bright, I am hap - py in the gos-pel light,
O I have that feel-ing in my soul, ev - er keep-ing me so free and whole,

FINE

Yes, I love to tell of my Sav-ior's love...............
And I love to tell .... of my Savior's love.

D.S.-And I love to tell .. .. of my Savior's love.

CHORUS

Love to tell the world of His love He has
I love to tell the world about His love For He has

I Love to Tell of His Love

Heaven's Nearer Ev'ry Day

R. J. W.

R. J. Weaver

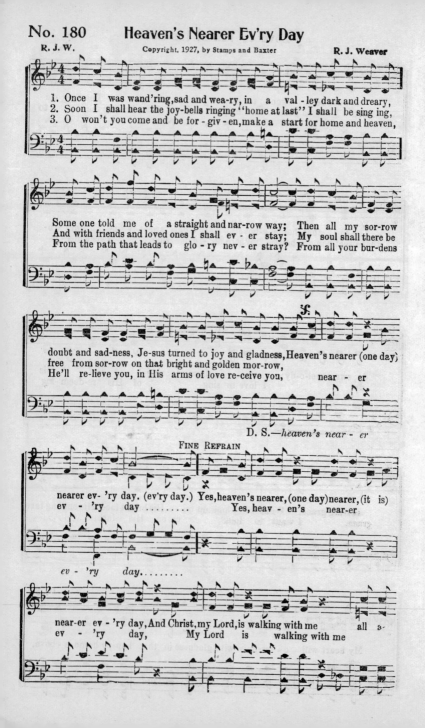

1. Once I was wand'ring, sad and wea-ry, in a val-ley dark and dreary,
2. Soon I shall hear the joy-bells ringing "home at last" I shall be sing ing,
3. O won't you come and be for-giv-en, make a start for home and heaven,

Some one told me of a straight and nar-row way; Then all my sor-row
And with friends and loved ones I shall ev-er stay; My soul shall there be
From the path that leads to glo-ry nev-er stray? From all your bur-dens

doubt and sad-ness, Je-sus turned to joy and gladness, Heaven's nearer (one day)
free from sor-row on that bright and golden mor-row,
He'll re-lieve you, in His arms of love re-ceive you, near - er

D. S.—*heaven's near - er*

FINE REFRAIN

nearer ev - 'ry day. (ev'ry day.) Yes, heaven's nearer, (one day) nearer, (it is)
ev - 'ry day .... Yes, heav - en's near-er

ev - 'ry day.......

near-er ev - 'ry day, And Christ, my Lord, is walking with me all a-
ev - 'ry day, My Lord is walking with me

long the way; I'm so hap-py, glad, and free for Je-sus gives me vic-to-ry, and

No. 181 I Want to Keep Telling the Story

Copyright, 1935, by C. L. Stewart in "Rays of Glory"

C. L. S.

C. L. STEWART

1. I want to keep tell-ing the sto-ry, How Je-sus from Heaven a-bove Came
2. He suffered and died on Mount Calv'ry, His life there so free-ly He gave; He
3. He then back to Heav-en as-cend-ed, But some day He's coming again; And
4. Then Sa-tan no lon-ger shall hin-der, Sweet peace o'er the earth then shall be; The

down from bright mansions of glo-ry, To prove to the world His great love. (great love.)
shed His life's blood in a-tone-ment, The world of lost sin-ners to save. (to save.)
those who are watching and wait-ing, A thousand years with Him shall reign. (shall reign.)
earth shall be full of His glo-ry, As wa-ters that cov-er the sea. (the sea.)

CHORUS

I want to keep tell-ing and sing-ing Of Je-sus the Sav-ior and King; ....

my King;

I want to be watching and wait-ing, For soon He is com-ing a-gain.

to earth a-gain.

In My Father's House Above

James Rowe   H. C. Collins, owner   H. C. Collins

DUET *Soprano and Tenor*

1. Just a-cross the si-lent riv-er, On a fair, e-ter-nal shore,
2. To this hap-py home I'm go-ing With the Friend who died for me,
3. I will trust, whate'er be-tide me, Strengthened by His mighty love,

I shall have a home for-ev-er With the Sav-ior I a-dore.
Who such love for me is show-ing, And who true to me will be.
Sure that He will keep and hide me From my foes till safe a-bove.

SOLO *Bass*

There no tempest will be sweep-ing, There no bur-den will be borne;
All the jour-ney may be drear-y, Bur-dens heav-y I may bear,
By and by my Lord will meet me, When on earth no more I roam,

There, in His e-ter-nal keep-ing, I shall spend an end-less morn.
Oft my spir-it may be wea-ry, But my Friend will lead me there.
With a lov-ing wel-come greet me, At the gates of "Home, sweet home."

CHORUS

There will bells of joy be ringing, There a glad, triumphant throng, Will, with rapture sweet, be

In My Father's House Above

sing-ing An un-end-ing joy-ous song; Hap-py I shall be for - ev - er In my

Father's house above, For fond hearts will never sever In that home of joy and love.

No. 183   Ever Since I Found Him

H. C. Collins, owner   H. C. Collins

1. God's dear Son has kept me singing Ev-er since I found Him; Kept my heart bells
2. O His love my life has brightened Ev-er since I found Him; Ev -'ry care and
3. Earth has been a place of pleas-ure Ev-er since I found Him, For my soul has

REFRAIN

sweet-ly ring-ing Ev-er since I found Him.
trou-ble lightened Ev-er since I found Him. Ever since that happy day When no
laid up treas-ure Ev-er since I found Him.

more I cared to stray, I have sung the days a-way Ev - er since I found Him.

No. 184 We'll Soon Be Done With Troubles And Trials

Dedicated to my father and mother Mr. and Mrs. J. T. Derricks—C. D.

C. D.

Cleavant Derricks

1. Some of these days I'm go - ing home where no sor - rows ev - er come,
2. Kin - dred and friends now wait for me, soon their fac - es I shall see,
3. I shall be - hold His bless - ed face, I shall feel His match-less grace,

We'll soon be done with troubles and tri-als; . . . .

We'll soon be done,

troubles and tri - als;

Safe from heart-ache, pain and care, we shall all that glo - ry share,
'Tis a home of life so fair and we'll all be gath - ered there,
O what peace and joy sub - lime in that home of love di - vine,

Sit down be - side my Je - sus,

sit down and

And I'm gon - na

Lord, I'm gon - na

Chorus

rest a lit - tle while.

We'll soon be done with trou-bles and

We'll soon be done,

We'll Soon Be Done With Troubles And Trials

tri - als,
Yes, in that home on the oth - er

troubles and tri - als In that home,

side,
Shake glad hands with the eld - ers,

on the oth - er side, And I'm a gon-na

tell my kin - dred good morn-ing,
Sit down be -

Lord, and
Then I'm gon - na

side my Je - sus,
gon - na sit down and rest a li'l while.....

Lord I'm

CODA*

Gon - na sit down and rest a li'l while........................

gon - na sit down and rest a li'l while.

*After last only

No. 185   Farther Along

As sung by BURNETTE SISTERS

1. Tempted and tried we're oft made to won-der Why it should be thus
2. When death has come and tak-en our loved ones, It leaves our home so
3. Faithful till death said our lov-ing Mas-ter, A few more days to
4. When we see Je-sus com-ing in glo-ry, When He comes from His

all the day long, While there are oth-ers liv-ing a-bout us,
lone-ly and drear; Then do we won-der why oth-ers pros-per,
la-bor and wait; Toils of the road will then seem as noth-ing,
home in the sky; Then we shall meet Him in that bright mansion,

CHORUS

Nev-er mo-lest-ed tho in the wrong.
Liv-ing so wick-ed year af-ter year.   Far-ther a-long we'll
As we sweep thru the beau-ti-ful gate.
We'll un-der-stand it all by and by.

know all a-bout it, Farther a-long we'll understand why; Cheer up, my

broth-er, live in the sun-shine, We'll understand it all by and by.

No. 186 When I Get to the End of the Way

CHARLIE D. TILLMAN

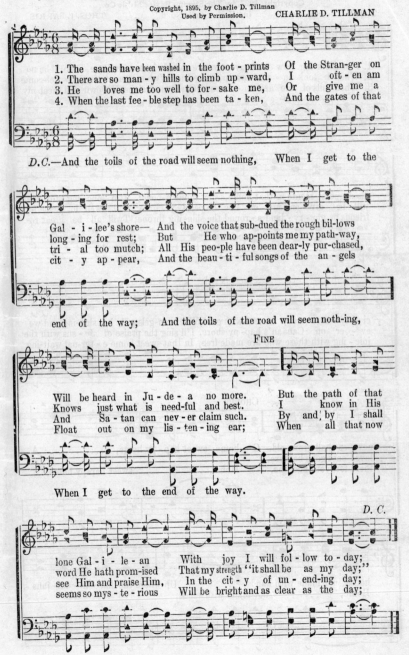

1. The sands have been washed in the foot-prints Of the Stran-ger on
2. There are so man-y hills to climb up-ward, I oft-en am
3. He loves me too well to for-sake me, Or give me a
4. When the last fee-ble step has been ta-ken, And the gates of that

D.C.—And the toils of the road will seem nothing, When I get to the

Gal-i-lee's shore— And the voice that sub-dued the rough bil-lows
long-ing for rest; But He who ap-points me my path-way,
tri-al too mutch; All His peo-ple have been dear-ly pur-chased,
cit-y ap-pear, And the beau-ti-ful songs of the an-gels

end of the way; And the toils of the road will seem noth-ing,

FINE

Will be heard in Ju-de-a no more. But the path of that
Knows just what is need-ful and best. I know in His
And Sa-tan can nev-er claim such. By and by I shall
Float out on my lis-ten-ing ear; When all that now

When I get to the end of the way.

D. C.

lone Gal-i-le-an With joy I will fol-low to-day;
word He hath prom-ised That my strength "it shall be as my day;"
see Him and praise Him, In the cit-y of un-end-ing day;
seems so mys-te-rious Will be bright and as clear as the day;

Home

T. J. F.   THOS. J. FARRIS

1. I'm think-ing now of heav-en where all is peace and love, There'll be no
2. When I look in-to heav-en, where friends who for me wait, A wel-come
3. When toils of life are o-ver and Christ shall claim His own, I'll meet my

dis-ap-point-ments in that home, sweet home a-bove; I'm long-ing for that
will be giv-en me in-side the pearl-y gate; I'll dwell in peace for-
friends in glo-ry-land a-round the shin-ing throne; 'Twill all be great re-

ci-ty where streets are paved with gold, Where an-gels will be sing-ing and we
ev-er on Canaan's hap-py shore, I'll sing the praise of Je-sus with the
joic-ing with those who are made free, In that sweet home e-ter-nal wait-ing

CHORUS

nev-er shall grow old. O home, sweet hap-py home, ... A
loved ones gone be-fore.
there for you and me. Home, ... sweet hap-py home,

house not made with hands, ... Up where the hal-le-lu-jahs
Home, ... not made with hands,

Home

roll;   I'll meet my loved ones there . . . . Where all   is
ev - er roll;   Home . . . . .   with loved ones there,   Home . . . .

bright and fair,   O hap - py home-land of   the soul. . . .
so bright and fair,

No. 188   What a Song We Shall Sing

Copyright, 1937, by The Stamps-Baxter Music Co.,
in "Harbor Bells No. 6"

S. M.   SAMUEL MUIER

1. When our work is complete and our loved ones we meet, What a song . . . .
2. We   shall all sing and shout when we lose ev'ry doubt,
3. When our burden's laid down and we take up our crown,   What a song

we shall sing;   All our trou-bles will end and our voic - es will blend,
If   to God we are true and His will strive to   do,
we shall sing; We shall gain perfect rest with the pure and the blest,

Saved by grace thru His love we'll reach heaven a - bove,

FINE   CHORUS   D. S.

What a song . . . .   we shall sing. What a song . . . .   we shall sing,
What a song   What a song   we shall sing,

Lord, Let Me Serve

Laurene Highfield   Virgil O. Stamps, owner   **Virgil O. Stamps**

Baritone Solo and Quartet

1. I do not ask for hap-py days, For eas-y tasks and
2. I do not long for high re-nown, I on-ly crave a
3. I do not ask for wealth or fame, But that I may not

joy-crowned ways, I on-ly ask that I may be   Of use, my
liv-ing crown, Set with the gems that I have earned, The souls of
put to shame, Nor cru-ci-fy my Lord a-new, By be-ing

CHORUS

Lord and Christ, to Thee.   Lord, let me serve . . . .
men from e-vil turned.   Lord, let me serve and faith-ful
faith-less or un-true. Lord, let me serve . . . .

. . . . . and faith-ful be, Lord, let me hum-bly fol - low
be,   Lord, let me hum-bly fol - low

Thee;   Make in Thy ranks   a place for me,
Thee; Make in Thy ranks . . . . . (a place for me . . . .)

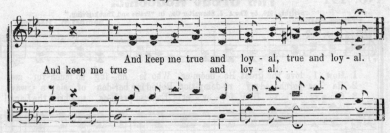

And keep me true and loy - al, true and loy - al.
And keep me true and loy - al....

No. 190   Love Divine Is Mine

James Rowe   C. D. Williams, owner   C. D. Williams

1. Hap - py songs I sing to - day, As I press a - long my way,
2. What are grief and care to me, If the Fount of love is free?
3. Hap - py songs are mine to - day, Hap - py songs will with me stay;

For this ran-somed soul of mine, O - ver-flows with love di - vine.
What are sor - row and dis - tress, If my Sav - ior waits to bless?
Joy will ev - er-more be mine, If I cling to love di - vine.

CHORUS

Love di - vine, re - deem - ing love! Pre-cious gift of God a - bove!

This my sweet - est song will be Thru the glad e - ter - ni - ty.

The Great Redeemer

Copyright, 1916, by The A. J. Showalter Co., in "Praise and Thanksgiving."

Francis Foster.   Samuel W. Beazley.

1. How I love the great Re-deem-er Who is do-ing so much for me;
2. He has purchased my re-demp-tion, Rolled my bur-den of sin a-way,
3. Glo-ry be to Him for-ev-er! Endless prais-es to Christ the Lamb!

With what joy I tell the sto-ry Of the love that makes men free. Till my
And is walk-ing on be-side me, Growing dear-er day by day. That is
He has filled my life with sunshine, He has made me what I am. O that

1. I will send   songs a-bove,

earth-ly life is end-ed, I will send   songs a-bove,
why I sing His prais-es, That is why   joy is mine,
ev-'ry one would know Him, O that all   would a-dore!

Then be-side the crys-tal sea More and more my soul shall be Prais-ing
That is why for ev-er-more On the ev-er-last-ing shore I shall
O that all would trust the love Of my might-y Friend a-bove And be

p Refrain.*

Je-sus and His love.
sing of love di-vine. He is ev-'ry-thing to me, to me, He is
His for ev-er-more.

* Bass to be sung loud. The other parts subdued and semi-staccato.

The Great Redeemer

He is ev - 'ry - thing to me, And ev - 'ry - thing shall
ev - 'ry-thing to me,...... And ev - 'ry-thing........ shall al-ways

al - ways be; I will nev - er cease to raise A
be; I will nev - er cease to raise...... A song of

song of glad - ness in His praise; Here, and in the
glad - ness in His praise; Here, and in........ the world a -

world a - bove, My soul shall sing of sav - ing love; Life and
bove,.... My soul shall sing...... of sav - ing love; Life and

Life and light and joy is He, The precious Friend who died for me.
light...... and joy is He,...... The precious Friend who died for me.

No. 192   I'd Like To Go Back

Slowly

Words and music by
Albert E. Brumley

1. Since I reached life's goal I'd like to stroll back to the fold, And explore the
2. In the ev'ning light In vis-ions quite my mind takes flight Back to days of
3. To her a-pron strings I'd like to cling and hear her sing, Sing to me some

days of yore By the lit - tle cab-in door; Since I went a-way I long and
hap - pi - ness And my mother's sweet caress; Time can-not e-rase Her fond em-
Lul - la - by Of those hap-py days gone by; Mother's sweet refrain, Each flow'ry

pray For YESTERDAY, The days that used to be More than all the world to me.
brace, Her smiling face, From the scenes of yesterday, In the good old-fashioned way.
lane Shall e'er re-main As a group of mel-o-dies In my book of memories.

REFRAIN

I'd like to go back......... to the dear old home....... And take an-oth-er look

at the mer-ry lit-tle brook Where I used to roam;...... I'd like to say "Hel-

I'd Like to Go Back

lo" .... to my mother don't you know, I'd like to live a-gain as I used to

live with-in that mer-ry lit-tle home; .... Oh, what a mem-'ry of

days that used to be, Oh, what a mem'ry— It seems but yes-terday,

I'd like to play a - round where I used to "Lie me down"

Rit. ....

When the whippoorwills were calling and the twilight shades were falling round the dear old home.

Its An Unfriendly World

A. E. B.
Albert E. Brumley

Slowly

1. Lord, I sometimes feel just like a stranger here, As I trav-el down life's road,
2. There are times when dis-appointments hover round, And the way seems dark and long,
3. Keep me, Lord, I pray and let Thy spir-it guide, As I wend my homeward way,

And no-bod-y knows the sorrow that I bear, Or how heav-y my load,
But the thought of heaven and a shin-ing crown, Keeps me singing a song;
As I tread life's val-ley be my shin-ing light, Be my shepherd and stay;

But in Thee, dear Lord, I have a precious friend, And my faith looks up to Thee,
I've no oth-er friend to lead me, blessed Lord, So I dai-ly cling to Thee,
Let me ev-er lean up-on Thy guiding arm, Till the lights of home I see,

Let me rise and go, for this dreary world below, Is an unfriendly world to me. (to me.)
Keep me lest I stray, from the straight and narrow way, It's an unfriendly world to me. (to me.)
Lord, I need Thy light, for this world of sin and night, Is an unfriendly world to me. (to me.)

CHORUS

Here I wan-der, like a beg-gar, thru the heat and the cold,
Here I've trod, on I plod, thru the heat and thru the cold,

Its An Unfriendly World

And my burdens are so heav-y Lord, my sorrow's untold,
Burdens here, hard to bear, Lord, my sorrow is untold,

But to Je-sus I am clinging, let me hide, Lord, in Thee,
Christ my King, I will cling, let me hide, dear Lord in Thee,

For this old world with it's sorrow, is an unfriendly world to me.
This old world, this old world to me.

No. 194   Meditation

Joseph Swain   Freeman Lewis

1. O, Thou in whose presence my soul takes delight, On whom in affliction I call;
2. Where dost Thou, dear Shepherd, resort with Thy sheep, To feed them in pastures of love?
3. O, why should I wan-der an al-ien from Thee, Or cry in the des-ert for bread?
4. Re-store, my dear Sav-iour, the light of Thy face, Thy soul-cheer-ing comfort impart;

My comfort by day and my song in the night, My hope, my sal-va-tion, my all.
Say, why in the valley of death should I weep, Or alone in this wil-der-ness rove?
Thy foes will rejoice when my sorrows they see, And smile at the tears I have shed.
And let the sweet tokens of pardoning grace, Bring joy to my des-o-late heart.

No. 195   Have Faith in God

J. R. Baxter, Jr.   Baxter and Upchurch, owners, 1928   H. E. Upchurch

1. We see the rain-bow shin-ing Up-on the dis-tant hill, We see the
2. The stars so bright a-bove us That cheer the gloomy night, Show God in
3. We can-not know the mean-ing Of all His works and ways, A veil is

vines en-twin-ing The boughs beside the rill; While gentle breezes fan them, 'Tis
heav'n does love us And bids us seek His light; You try to find some oth-er Such
in - ter-ven-ing Thru-out our earthly days; He left His word to guide us A-

won-der-ful and grand, It took our God to plan them, And un - der-stand.
wonders to per-form, You seek in vain, my brother, He stills the storm.
long the pil-grim road, His Spir-it walks be-side us To share our load.

REFRAIN

Have faith.... in God, the Fa - ther, Have faith in Christ, the Son,
Have faith in God, the Father, and Have faith in Christ, His on ly Son,
Have faith.... in Him who gave you, When Christ to Cal-v'ry trod,
Have faith in Him who gave to you, When Christ alone to Calv'ry trod,

No harm can ever both - er The soul with Christ made one;
Such priceless love to save you, (Omit . . . .) Have faith in God.

No. 196   I Heard My Mother Call My Name in Prayer

TO MY MOTHER

E. M. B.   Copyright, 1919, by E. M. Bartlett   E. M. Bartlett

May be used as Soprano and Alto Duet

1. While kneeling by her bed-side in the cot-tage on the hill, My
2. She was an-xious for her boy to be just what he ought to be   And she
3. How my heart was touched and tendered by the pray'r that mother prayed! I can
4. Then I gave my heart to Je - sus and am liv-ing now for Him   And some

moth-er prayed her blessings on me there; She was talk-ing then to Je - sus
asked the Lord to take Him in His care; Just the words I can't re-mem-ber
al - most see her form now kneeling there As she told her Lord and Sav-ior
day I'll go to meet Him in the air; For He heard my mother pray-ing

while ev-'ry-thing was still And I heard my mother call my name in pray'r.
but I know she prayed for me, For I heard my mother call my name in pray'r.
just how far from Him I strayed, Yes, I heard my mother call my name in pray'r.
and has saved my soul from sin Yes, He heard my mother call my name in pray'r.

Fine

D.S.-and He saved my soul from sin For He heard my mother call my name in pray'r.

Chorus

Yes, I heard my moth - er call my name in pray'r, She was

D.S.

pour-ing out her heart to Je - sus there, Then I gave my heart to Him

That Little Old Hut Was a Mansion to Me.

E. M. B.

E. M. Bartlett.

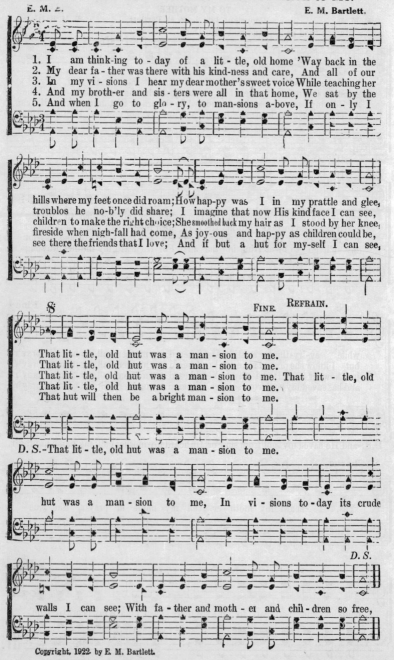

1. I am think-ing to-day of a lit-tle, old home 'Way back in the
2. My dear fa-ther was there with his kind-ness and care, And all of our
3. In my vi-sions I hear my dear mother's sweet voice While teaching her
4. And my broth-er and sis-ters were all in that home, We sat by the
5. And when I go to glo-ry, to man-sions a-bove, If on-ly I

hills where my feet once did roam; How hap-py was I in my prattle and glee,
troublos he no-b'ly did share; I imagine that now His kind face I can see,
children to make the right choice; She smoothed back my hair as I stood by her knee,
fireside when nigh-fall had come, As joy-ous and hap-py as children could be,
see there the friends that I love; And if but a hut for my-self I can see,

FINE. REFRAIN.

That lit-tle, old hut was a man-sion to me.
That lit-tle, old hut was a man-sion to me.
That lit-tle, old hut was a man-sion to me. That lit-tle, old
That lit-tle, old hut was a man-sion to me.
That hut will then be a bright man-sion to me.

D. S.—That lit-tle, old hut was a man-sion to me.

hut was a man-sion to me, In vi-sions to-day its crude

D. S.

walls I can see; With fa-ther and moth-er and chil-dren so free,

No. 198   Mother's Bible

Rev. W. P. Long   Frank H. Stamps

1. I dear-ly love ..... my mother's book, ... The one she read ......
2. My mother taught .... me in my youth .... To live for Christ, ...
3. This book is for ...... the young and old, ... 'Twill cheer us in ......
4. The best of all, ... the most sub-lime, ... I know my sins ....

and stained with tears; .... Her pray'rs, her love ..... and ten-der look ......
lest I should stray ...... And leave the light .... of sav-ing truth, ...
the lone-ly hour; .... It will re-vive .... the heart when cold ....
are now for-giv'n; ..... I'm trust-ing in .... this book di-vine

rit.   FINE CHORUS *a tempo*

Have followed me ..... thru all these years .....   I want to hear
And miss the good ..... old Bi ble way .....
Like dew up-on .... the thirst-y flow'r ....
To guide my soul ..... from earth to heav'n . I want to hear ....

D.S.—When we were all ..... to-geth-er there ......

her voice once more   And kneel with her in one more
her voice once more ...... And kneel with her

D. S.

pray'r,   Just like a child   in days of yore,
in one more pray'r Just like a child ...... in days of yore,

No. 199 — There's a Little Pine Log Cabin

Copyright, 1937, by The Stamps-Baxter Music Co.

A. E. B.
Slow
ALBERT E. BRUMLEY

1. There's a lit-tle pine log cab-in Wait-in' down in Wel-come Val-ley, There's an o-pen door and when my roamin's o'er I'm go-in' back home; There's a moth-er dai-ly pray-in', Wait-in' for my home-ward stray-in' To that lit-tle pine log cab-in, Nev-er-more to roam.

2. Oft-en when a-lone I still dream Of the days be-side the mill-stream With my dad and moth-er and my lit-tle broth-er Hap-py and gay; I can see the shad-ows fall-in' And I hear their voi-ces call-in' From that lit-tle pine log cab-in At the end of the way.

3. There's a lit-tle lamp-light shin-in', There's a lit-tle trail a wind-in' Down a lit-tle val-ley to that lit-tle cab-in, Peace-ful and still; Hon-ey-suc-kle vines are grow-in' And I know I'll soon be go-in' To that lit-tle pine log cab-in At the foot of the hill.

There's a Little Pine Log Cabin

CHORUS

I want to see the chil-dren play-in', By the weep-in' wil-lows stray-in', Hear my moth-er soft-ly pray-in' While the mock-ing birds sing; How my wea-ry heart is so sweet-ly; yearn-in' Just to be a-gain re-turn-in' To that lit-tle pine log cab-in in the land of my dreams.

Who?

W. A. McK.

Wm. A. McKinney

1. Who (O who) went to Calv'ry's cross?.............. Who (O who)
2. Who (O who) is this might-y friend?................. Who (O who)
3. Who (O who) hears us when we pray?................. O Who (O who)

counted wealth as dross?........... Who suffered ag - o - ny, who set the
died for sin - ful men?.............. Who had for us such love, who left His
keeps us day dy day?............. Who's coming back again, a thousand

cap-tive free? Who but the man of Gal - i - lee? (the man of Gal - i - lee?)
home a-bove? Who wore the crown of thorns below? (the crown of thorns below?)
years to reign? Who is this mighty friend divine? (this mighty friend divine?)

Who (O who) made the sac - ri - fice?.................... for sin - ners?
Who (O who) in the new tomb lay?.................... my Sav - ior,
Who (O who) saves a soul that's lost?.................... in dark-ness?

Who?

Who (O who) paid so great a price?............. but Je - sus? Whose blood came
Who (O who) rolled the stone away? .... for Je - sus? Who rose up
Who (O who) paid for you the cost?..... ....'twas Je-sus, Trust Him, dear

from His side, who suffered, bled and died? Je - sus my Lord who died for
from the dead in three days, as He said? No one but Je - sus Christ, I
sin - ner friend, He'll keep you to the end, Je - sus this lov - ing friend of

CHORUS

me. (for me.)
know. (I know.) Who watches o - ver you,
mine. (of mine.) who is a friend so true?

Whose spir-it comforts you each passing day?....... Who is it you go to
who loves you?

when you are feeling blue? Je-sus, 'tis Je - sus who drives blues a-way. (a-way.)

No. 201   My Dream-Home in Glory

Copyright, 1937, by The Stamps-Baxter Music Co.

Rev. W. A. WASHBURN   VIRGIL O. STAMPS

1. There's a won-der-ful dream-home in glo-ry, "In a land where we'll
2. In that dream-home of mine o-ver yon-der, Not a thing that I
3. O that dream-home of mine o-ver yon-der, It is more than just

nev-er grow old," That we've heard of in song and in sto-ry, "'Tis a
need is de-nied, Oft-en times in my dreams do I pon-der, Pear-ly
mere-ly a dream, It is not just a sad dis-al-lu-sion, Like our

ci-ty whose streets are pure gold; Here on earth I'm a lone, wea-ry
gates that now stand o-pen wide; There the ros-es are bloom-ing e-
fond-est hopes here some-time seem; For my Sav-ior has gone to make

pil-grim, And I know I don't have long to stay, But I'll set-tle in
ter-nal, And no dark dis-ap-pointments will come, All my prayers of the
read-y, Man-y man-sions for all who will come, He has made me a

glo-ry for-ev-er, In my dream-home just o-ver the way.
past will be answered, When I'm safe in my hap-py dream-home.
ti-tle in glo-ry To my hap-py e-ter-nal dream-home.

My Dream-Home in Glory

Chorus

Won-der-ful dream-home, dream-home in glo - ry, Where all of my
O my dream - - home in glo - ry, Where all

dreams will come true, Beautiful dream-home, dream-home in glory,
of my dreams will come true, O my dream home in glo-ry,

Some day I would share it with you; We can live in that dream-land for-
Some day I would share it with you;

ev - er, In that home where we'll nev-er be blue, Why
In that home where we'll nev-er be blue,

don't you arrange it with Je - sus And make it your dream-home, too?
And make it your dream-home, too?

No. 202   Holy Be Thy Great Name

SPIRITUAL

Copyright, 1938, by The Stamps-Baxter Music Co.

J. B. C. and J. R. B.

J. B. Coats

Ho-ly be, ho-ly be, ho-ly be thy name,   Ho-ly be

for-ev-er,

ho-ly be, ho-ly be thy name;

for-ev-er;

1. Let Thy ban-ner be unfurled
2. Let me tell Thy matchless love,
3. Let me make the glad tones ring,

o-ver all the world, Ho-ly be, ho-ly be, ho-ly be thy name.
com-ing from a-bove,
prais-es ev-er sing,

matchless name.

Chorus

Ho-ly, ho-ly,   ho-ly, ho-ly,   Ho-ly be Thy great
Ho - - - ly,   ho - - - ly,   Ho - ly

name;   Ho-ly, ho-ly,   ho-ly, ho-ly,   Ho-ly
Ho - - ly,   ho - - ly,   Ho - ly

Holy Be Thy Great Name

be Thy great name. Hal-le-lu, hal-le-lu,
Hal-le-lu - - jah, hal-le-lu - - jah, Hal-le-

Hal-le-lu, and a-men; Ho-ly, ho-ly,
lu - - jah, a - men; for-ev-er; Ho - - - ly,

ho-ly, ho-ly, Ho-ly be Thy great name.
ho - - - - - ly, Ho-ly

No. 203 My Faith Looks Up To Thee

Ray Palmer   Lowell Mason

1. My faith looks up to Thee, Thou Lamb of Cal-va-ry, Sav-ior di-vine; Now hear me
2. May Thy rich grace impart Strength to my fainting heart, My zeal in-spire; As Thou hast
3. While life's dark maze I tread And grief around me spread, Be Thou my Guide; Bid darkness

while I pray, Take all my sins a-way, O let me from this day Be whol-ly Thine!
died for me, O may my love to Thee Pure, warm and changeless be, A liv-ing fire!
turn to day, Wipe sorrow's tears away, Nor let me ev - er stray From Thee aside.

No. 204   He Said If I Be Lifted Up

C. E. P. Arr. by J. R. B., Jr.   Chas. H. Pace, Arr. by V. O. Stamps

1. Down in the val-ley while on my knees I asked my Je-sus hear me
2. My Je-sus told me, when things go wrong, Just keep on pray-ing all day
3. When I am lone-ly, when I am sad, My Je-sus comes and makes me

please, He promised that He'd take care of me, If I would lift Him up.
long, I'll fight your battles, I'll make you strong, If you will lift me up.
glad; He is the dear-est friend I have had, I want to lift Him up.

Chorus

He said if I be lift-ed up, He said if
He said if I be lift-ed up,

I be lift-ed up; I'll be your fa-ther, I'll
He said if I be lift-ed up;

be your mother, I'll be your sis-ter and your brother,
brother, He said if

He Said If I Be Lifted Up

He said if I be lift-ed up, I'll bring joy to your soul.
be lifted up, joy, joy

No. 205   I Know My Name Is There

Luke 10: 20.

D. S. WARNER
CONTROLLED BY R. E. WINSET
R. E. WARREN

1. My name is in the Book of Life, O bless the name of Je - sus!
2. My name once stood with sinners, lost, And bore a pain-ful rec - ord;
3. Yet in-ward troub-le oft - en cast A shad-ow o'er my ti - tle;
4. While oth-ers climb thro' worldly strife, To carve a name of hon - or,

I rise a-bove all doubt and strife, And read my ti - tle clear.
But by His blood the Sav - ior cross'd, And placed it on His roll.
But now with full sal - va - tion blest, Praise God! it's ev - er clear.
High up in heav-en's Book of Life, My name is writ - ten there.

Chorus

I know,........ I know........ my name........ is there; is there;
I know, I tru - ly know, I know my name is there;

I know,...... I know........ my name is writ - ten there.
I know my name is there,

Ring, Merry Bells

James Rowe   Samuel W. Beazley

1. Ring, mer - ry bells, for your mu - sic of cheer Al - ways is glad,
2. Ring, mer - ry bells, for the hearts that are sad, Fill them with joy;
3. Ring, mer - ry bells, fill the mo-ments with joy, Peal aft - er peal,

ten - der and sweet; Peal aft - er peal, mer - ry bells, let us hear,
com - fort be - stow; Cause them to feel that the world still is glad,
chime aft - er chime; All your sweet mu - sic this morn ing em - ploy,

Chorus

For they will give us glad-ness complete. Ring, merry, mer - ry bells,
Help them the sweet-est pleas-ures to know. Ring,............ mer - ry
Give to us all the hap - pi - est time. Ring, ring, ring bells,

ring, mer - ry, mer - ry bells, Ring, ring,
bells,............... Send your strains o - ver all the hills and the
ring, ring, ring bells, Ring, ring, ring, ring,

ring,................. Ring. O ring, mer - ry, mer - ry bells,
plains, o - ver all the dells; Give................ out your
ring, ring, ring, ring, Ring, ring, ring bells,

Ring, Merry Bells

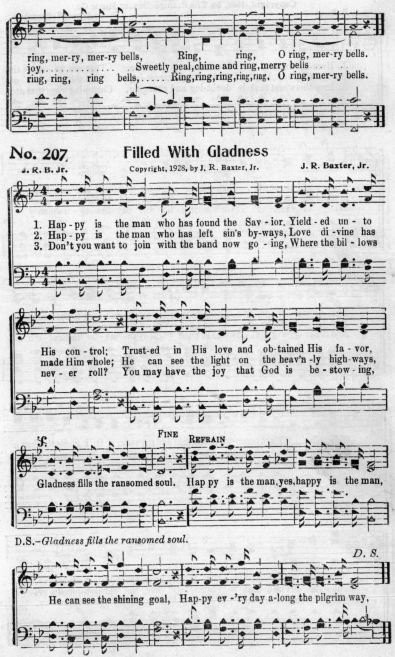

ring, mer-ry, mer-ry bells, Ring, ring, O ring, mer-ry bells.
joy,.............. Sweetly peal, chime and ring, merry bells ...
ring, ring, ring bells,..... Ring, ring, ring, ring, ring, O ring, mer-ry bells.

No. 207 Filled With Gladness

J. R. B. Jr.

Copyright, 1928, by J. R. Baxter, Jr.

J. R. Baxter, Jr.

1. Hap-py is the man who has found the Sav-ior, Yield-ed un-to
2. Hap-py is the man who has left sin's by-ways, Love di-vine has
3. Don't you want to join with the band now go-ing, Where the bil-lows

His con-trol; Trust-ed in His love and ob-tained His fa-vor,
made Him whole; He can see the light on the heav'n-ly high-ways,
nev-er roll? You may have the joy that God is be-stow-ing,

FINE   REFRAIN

Gladness fills the ransomed soul. Hap-py is the man, yes, happy is the man,

D.S.—*Gladness fills the ransomed soul.*

D. S.

He can see the shining goal, Hap-py ev-'ry day a-long the pilgrim way,

No. 208 I Guess I'm Just a Little Old Fashioned

A. E. B.

Albert E. Brumley

1. Here so man-y are break-ing tra-di-tions That are sa-cred the whole world a-round, Seek-ing on-ly for rich-es and pleasures That so free-ly in this life a-bound; But I still love the pre-cious old Bi-ble, 'Tis my com-fort, my guide and my stay, O I guess I'm just a lit-tle old fashioned But I still love the old fash-ioned way.

2. O they say I'm old fashioned for trust-ing In the sto-ry of long, long a-go, And they say I've an old fashioned fan-cy Just be-cause I be-lieve it is so; Well, the whole world can call me old fash-ioned, They can call me what-ev-er they may, But I'll still be just a lit-tle old fashioned For I still love the old fash-ioned way.

3. In this world that is doubt-ing and changing, Chang-ing ways that are old for the new, There's a need for the old time re-li-gion And the pray'rs of the Christians so true; May the Sav-ior who rul-eth in heav-en Hear the old fashioned pray'rs that we pray, May He keep us just a lit-tle old fashioned For I still love the old fash-ioned way.

I Guess I'm Just a Little Old Fashioned

Chorus

O I guess I'm just a lit - tle old fashioned, But I still love the old fashioned way, Lord, I care not for the world and its glo - ry, Or the life that is mod-ern and gay; But I still love the songs a - bout Je - sus And I still love the Bi - ble so true, O I guess I'm just a lit - tle old fash-ioned, But my Sav - ior was old fashioned, too.

NO SHADOWS

A. M. P.

ADEGR M. PACE.

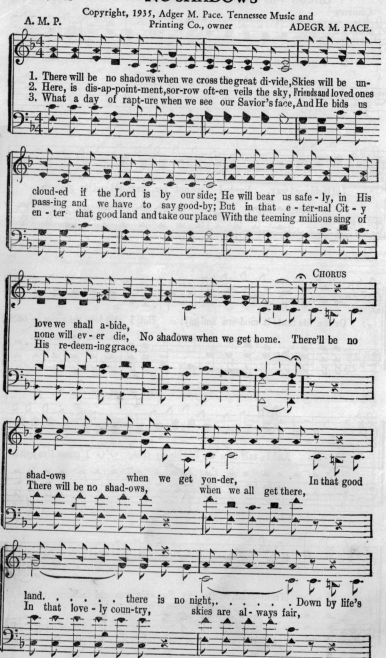

1. There will be no shadows when we cross the great di-vide, Skies will be un-
2. Here, is dis-ap-point-ment, sor-row oft-en veils the sky, Friends and loved ones
3. What a day of rapt-ure when we see our Savior's face, And He bids us

cloud-ed if the Lord is by our side; He will bear us safe-ly, in His
pass-ing and we have to say good-by; But in that e-ter-nal Cit-y
en-ter that good land and take our place With the teeming millions sing of

CHORUS

love we shall a-bide,
none will ev-er die, No shadows when we get home. There'll be no
His re-deem-ing grace,

shad-ows   when we get yon-der,   In that good
There will be no shad-ows,   when we all get there,

land. . . . . there is no night, ... Down by life's
In that love-ly coun-try,   skies are al-ways fair,

NO SHADOWS

riv - er, love will grow fonder, For there the Sun . . . .
By the crystal riv-er, riv-er of de-light, There the Sun is

. . . . is al-ways bright; In that fair E-den we'll
shin-ing, al-ways shining bright; In that love-ly E-den,

live for - ev - er, O'er fields e - ly-sian, we'll glad-ly
free from ev'-ry care, Roam the fields e - ly-sian,

roam, ... 'Twill all be glo-ry, oh, hal - le - lu-jah,
with the an-gels fair, It will all be glo-ry, 'neath the heav'n-ly dome,

There'll be no shad-ows when we get home.
There will be no shad-ows when we get home, when we get home.

A Beautiful Prayer

L. G. P.   LUTHER G. PRESLEY

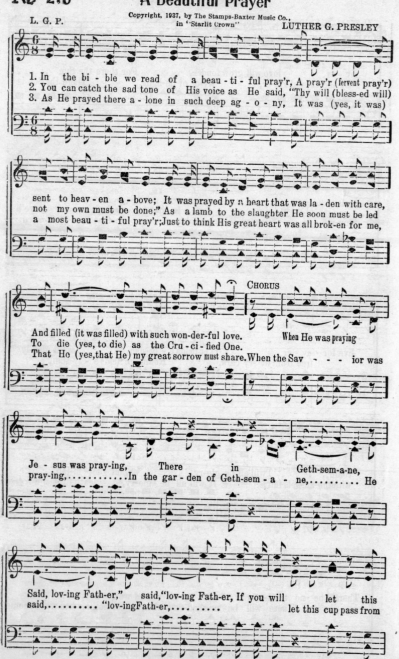

1. In the bi - ble we read of a beau - ti - ful pray'r, A pray'r (fervent pray'r)
2. You can catch the sad tone of His voice as He said, "Thy will (bless-ed will)
3. As He prayed there a - lone in such deep ag - o - ny, It was (yes, it was)

sent to heav - en a - bove; It was prayed by a heart that was la - den with care,
not my own must be done;" As a lamb to the slaughter He soon must be led
a most beau - ti - ful pray'r; Just to think His great heart was all brok-en for me,

CHORUS

And filled (it was filled) with such won-der-ful love.   When He was praying
To die (yes, to die) as the Cru - ci - fied One.   When the Sav - - - ior was
That He (yes, that He) my great sorrow must share.

Je - sus was pray-ing,   There   in   Geth-sem-a-ne,
pray-ing,............In the gar - den of Geth-sem - a - ne,............He

Said, lov-ing Fath-er,"   said, "lov-ing Fath-er, If you will   let   this
said,.......... "lov-ingFath-er,.... .....   let this cup pass from

A Beautiful Prayer

cup pass from me;" Know He was thinking, know He was thinking,
me;".......... I know He was think-ing......... Of the

Grief death would bring to His own, Deep was His sor-row,
anguish death would bring to His own,..... .... How deep......... was His

deep was His sor-row, When He was pray-ing a-lone.
sor-row,..... .....When Je-sus was pray-ing a-lone.............

No. 211   Lost in Eternity's Night

W. H DAVIS   THURMAN H. SMITH

1. I am not read-y if Je-sus should call, I've taken no time to pre-pare;
2. I have been bus-y in gath-er-ing in Of per-ish-ing silver and gold,
3. Age is up-on me and still I am lost, No way to escape my just doom;

CHORUS –Lost and un-worth-y of God's purest love, I'm lost from that heaven of light;

And un-der His judgment I sure-ly will fall, I'd shrink from His presence up there.
For-get-ting the Sav-ior and rev'ling in sin, Re-fus-ing to en-ter the fold.
On beds of re-flec-tion I'm sleeplessly tossed, My soul is o'erburdened with gloom.

I'll nev-er be-hold all His glo-ries a-bove, But lost in e-ter-ni-ty's night.

No. 212   This World is Not My Home

(I'm Just A Passing Thru)

Arr. by
ALBERT E. BRUMLEY

Arr. copyrighted by Albert E. Brumley

1. This world is not my home, I'm just a pass-ing thru; My treasures are laid
2. They're all ex-pect-ing me, And that's one thing I know, I fixed it up with
3. I have a lov-ing moth-er o-ver in glo-ry land, I don't ex-pect to
4. Just o-ver in glo-ry land We'll live e-ter-nal-ly, The saints on ev-'ry

up Somewhere beyond the blue; The an-gels beck-on me From heaven's o-pen door,
Je-sus fort-y years a-go; I know He'll take me thru Tho I am weak and poor,
stop Un-til I shake her hand; She's wait-ing now for me In heaven's o-pen door,
hand Are shouting vic-to-ry; Their songs of sweetest praise Drift back from heaven's shore,

FINE REFRAIN

And I can't feel at home in this world an-y-more. O Lord, you know I

have no friend like you, If heav-en's not my home then Lord, what will I

D. S.

do; The an-gels beck-on me from heav-en's o-pen door, And I

No. 213 I Don't Want to Get Adjusted
(To this world)

S. J. M. OWNED BY SANFORD J. MASSENGALE Sanford J. Massengale

1. In this world we have our troubles, Sometimes lonesome, sometimes blue;
2. Lord I'm growing worn and weary, There's no place that seems like home;
3. I am long-ing for the com-ing, Of my Sav-ior Lord and King;

But the hope of life e-ter-nal, Brigh-tens all our hopes a-new.
Je-sus come my soul to fer-ry, Where I nev-er more shall roam.
Seems I hear my loved ones sing-ing, A new song I'd like to sing.

REFRAIN

I don't want...... to get ad-just-ed........ ....to this world,
I don't want to get ad-just-ed, get ad-just-ed to this world,

to this world, I've got a home that's so much bet-ter, I want to
to this world,

go to sooner or lat-er, I don't want to get ad-justed to this world.

Jewels for His Crown.

James Rowe.

Samuel W. Beazley.

1. While the sunshine floods with splendor All the hills and the val-leys of life,
2. From the narrow lanes and by-ways, From the plains and the val-leys of sin,
3. At the gates our Lord will meet us, If to Him precious jewels we bear;

Faith-ful serv-ice let us ren-der, Let us wage a no-ble strife;
From the noi-sy, bu-sy high-ways, Let us bring the jew-els in.
With a smile our King will greet us, When we reach that kingdom fair.

Let there be no more re-pin-ing, Let us ban-ish the sigh and the frown;
Here is one, and there a clus-ter, Precious jew-els for which He came down;
If we wish to share His glo-ry, When the burdens of life are laid down;

While the sun of life is shin-ing, Gath-er jew-els for His crown.
They have lost their ear-ly lus-tre, But are jew-els for His crown.
We must tell the grand old sto-ry—Gath-er jew-els for His crown.

Chorus.

Gath-er jew-els for His crown, Gath-er jew-els
Gath-er jew - - - els for His

Jewels for His Crown.

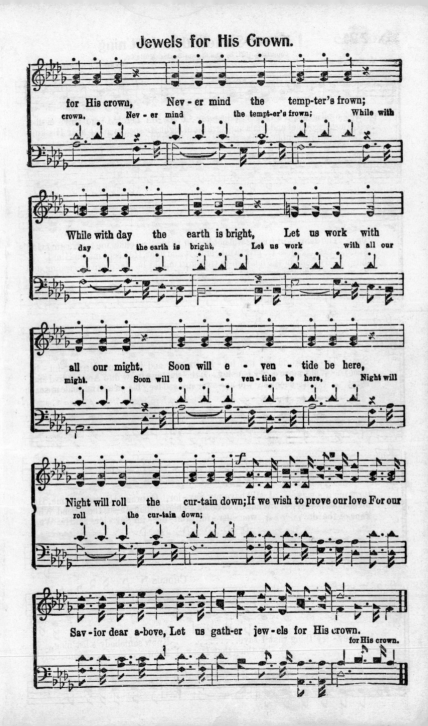

for His crown, Nev - er mind the temp-ter's frown;
crown, Nev - er mind the tempt-er's frown; While with

While with day the earth is bright, Let us work with
day the earth is bright, Let us work with all our

all our might. Soon will e - ven - tide be here,
might. Soon will e - - - ven-tide be here, Night will

Night will roll the cur-tain down; If we wish to prove our love For our
roll the cur-tain down;

Sav - ior dear a-bove, Let us gath-er jew-els for His crown.
for His crown.

No. 215 I Know Somebody's List'ning

A. E. B.

ALBERT E. BRUMLEY

1. Tho a pil-grim, a stranger, a beg-gar I be As here I go trav-el-ing
2. Thru the troubles and trials and darkest of night He speaks and I hear His kind
3. Let the world amble on like the Bab'lon of old With beau-ty and charm to al-

on, Tho dearest of friends will not lis-ten to me And chide me for trusting God's
voice, Thru darkness He giveth me comfort and light, He keeps me, in Him I re-
lure, My hope in the heav-en-ly treasures untold Is far more ex-ceeding and

Son; Tho the world in its fol-ly, its sin and its shame, Neglect-ful-ly
joice; What more could I ask when the shadows grow dim And kindred and
sure; My Re-deem-er will an-swer my sad fee-ble plea And guide me each

turns me a-way, I still have my Sav-ior, O praise His sweet name, He
loved ones betray, What more could I cherish than Je-sus the Friend Who
hour of the day, A won-der-ful, won-der-ful Sav-ior is He Who

CHORUS

hears ev-'ry thing that I say.......... Know somebody's list'ning,
ev-'ry thing that I say. I know.......... somebody's

I Know Somebody's List'ning

know somebody's list'-ning, Hears ev - 'ry thing that I say,
list'-ning.......... And hears ev -'ry thing that I say, ... I

Know somebody answers, know somebody answers, Pray'r
know............ some-bod-y an-swers.......... Ev-'ry pray'r that I

that I se - cret - ly pray; Know somebody loves me know somebody
se - cret - ly pray; .... I know.......... some-bod-y loves me......

loves me, Nev - er will turn me a - way, Je - - -
...... And nev - er will turn me a - way,.......... 'Tis Je - sus the

sus of Mount Calvary And He hears ev'ry thing that I say..........
Sav - ior of ev'ry thing that I say.

No. 216 Gettin' Ready to Leave This World

Spiritual

Copyright, 1937, by The Stamps-Baxter Music Co.,
in "Starlit Crown"

L. G. P.

LUTHER G. PRESLEY

1. Lay-ing up my treasures in that home above, Trusting, fully trusting in the
2. Trust-ing in the rich-es of His sav-ing grace, In each earthly tri-al I His
3. To pre-pare a man-sion, Je-sus said, "I'll go, If it were not true I would have

Sav-ior's love; Do-ing what I can for heaven's Ho-ly Dove,
love can trace; Sure that up in heav-en I shall find a place, I'm a get-tin'
told you so;" Just a lit-tle while to lin-ger here be-low,

CHORUS

read-y to leave this world. Gettin' read-y to
to leave this I'm a get-tin' ready to
Get-tin' read-y, gettin' ready

Read-y to

leave this world, Get-tin' read-y for the
leave this world of sor-row, I'm a get-tin' read-y
to leave this world, Get-tin' read-y for the

leave this world of sor-row, Read-y, get-tin'

Gettin' Ready to Leave This World

gates of pearl; Keep-ing, watch-ing, both
for the gates of pearl; my re-cord bright,

read-y for the gates of pearl tomorrow;

Gettin' read - y to leave this world.
I'm a get - tin' read-y to leave this sin-ful world.
day and night, Gettin' ready now

Read - y to leave this world.

No. 217   Came Into my Heart to Stay

Copyright, 1937, by The Stamps-Baxter Music Co.,
"In Starlit Crown"

REV. B. B. EDMIASTON   MARVIN P. DALTON

1. A mess-age of love from heaven a-bove
2. My pleading He heard, the pow'r of His word Came into my heart to stay,
3. The rap-ture of love like heav-en above

A sense of my need of some-one to lead
Sal - va-tion is mine, His par-don di-vine Came in-to my heart to stay.
The Spir-it di-vine bears witness with mine,

FINE

D.S.—The Spir - it di - vine bears witness with mine, Came into my heart to stay.

CHORUS   D.S.

Came in - to my heart, 'twill nev-er de-part, Came in-to my heart to stay;

Get Ready for That Day

SPIRITUAL

G. C.

GRADY COLE

1. Some folks don't ev-er read the Bi-ble, Some folks don't ever kneel and pray;
2. Some day this world with fire'll be burning, Some day when Jesus comes again;
3. Some day this world will be in darkness, Some day the stars be-gin to fall;

Some folks make light of me for shouting, But I'm gon-na keep shouting an-y-
Some- one will be left here in sor-row, Then somebody will call my Savior's
Some day that old moon will be bleeding, I'm happy be-cause Je-sus is my

way. I care not what they say a-bout me, Je-sus will guide me safely on;
name. Some-one will say: "O Lord, have mercy," When Gabr'el blows that trumpet loud;
all. Some folks may say that I'm just talking, Some folks may laugh at what I say;

And some day He'll take me home to glory, Some-one will be left here to mourn.
But I will be shouting hal-le-lu-jah, When Jesus comes down in a cloud.
But some day some-one will be so sor-ry, Brother, get read-y for that day.

CHORUS

Some-bod-y's gon-na wish they had re-lig-ion, Some-bod-y's gon-na wish they

Get Ready for That Day

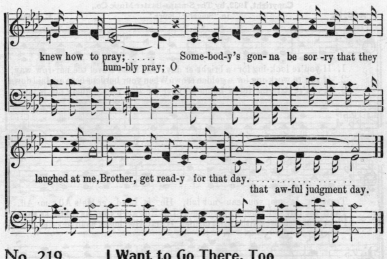

knew how to pray; ..... Some-bod-y's gon-na be sor-ry that they
hum-bly pray; O

laughed at me, Brother, get read-y for that day. ....
that aw-ful judgment day.

No. 219 I Want to Go There, Too

SPIRITUAL

M. S. H.   M. S. HALL

1. When I shall reach the gold-en shore, I want to go there,
2. When Je - sus took my sins a - way, I want to go there,
3. When I shall cross the stormy sea, I want to go there,

too;   I'll live with loved ones gone be - fore, I
My soul was cleansed on that glad day, I
hal - le - lu - jah, Lord, From toil and care I'll be set free, I

I want to live with all things new,

FINE   CHORUS   D. S.

want to go there, too. O Lord I want to go, I want to go, Lord,

No. 220
Look Up

A. C. D.

A. C. Doss

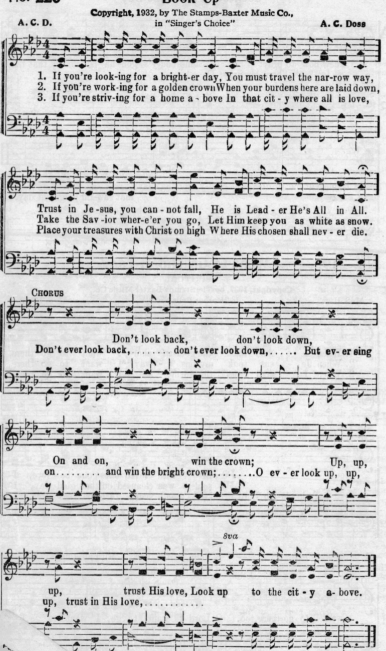

1. If you're look-ing for a bright-er day, You must travel the nar-row way,
2. If you're work-ing for a golden crown When your burdens here are laid down,
3. If you're striv-ing for a home a-bove In that cit-y where all is love,

Trust in Je-sus, you can-not fall, He is Lead-er He's All in All.
Take the Sav-ior wher-e'er you go, Let Him keep you as white as snow.
Place your treasures with Christ on high Where His chosen shall nev-er die.

CHORUS

Don't look back, don't look down,
Don't ever look back,........ don't ever look down,...... But ev-er sing

On and on, win the crown; Up, up,
on......... and win the bright crown;........O ev-er look up, up,

up, trust His love, Look up to the cit-y a-bove.
up, trust in His love,............

Index